PUBLICATIONS OF
THE NATIONAL ROSE SOCIETY

"THE ROSE ANNUAL." This is issued early in each year, and contains articles and illustrations of interest to all Rosarians. 200 pages and 16 colour plates. *Published at 8/6.*

"ROSES: THE CULTIVATION OF THE ROSE." Part I tells how to prepare the rose beds; how to plant and care for the rose trees, with methods of pruning, general cultivation, fertilising, protection from pest and disease and propagation by cuttings and budding. Part II contains short scientific extracts from "The Enemies of the Rose" by John Ramsbottom, O.B.E., M.A., Dr. Sc. *Published at 5/-.*

"ROSES: A SELECTED LIST OF VARIETIES." Illustrated. This list contains descriptions of the best Roses in cultivation, and also the purposes for which each variety is best suited. *Published at 5/-.*

"THE ENEMIES OF THE ROSE." Illustrated in colours and bound in cloth. A scientific treatise on the Insect Pests and Diseases of the Rose. This publication has now been withdrawn from general distribution but may be obtained on loan from the library. A limited number are available for purchase by members.

Extra copies of the above Publications can be obtained by Members direct from :

THE SECRETARY,
BONE HILL, CHISWELL GREEN LANE, ST. ALBANS,
HERTFORDSHIRE.

Telephone : LN 50461 (St. Albans).

THE NATIONAL ROSE SOCIETY.—All interested in Rose Culture are invited to join this Society. There is no ballot for membership. The Annual Subscription is £1 1s. or 10/6. *The Publications are supplied to new Members free of charge.* Application for membership should be made to the Secretary, Bone Hill, Chiswell Green Lane, St. Albans, Hertfordshire. New Members also receive tickets for London and Provincial Shows.

Roses

THE CULTIVATION OF
THE ROSE

by

BERTRAM PARK, O.B.E., V.M.H., *Mérite Agri.*

Produced by the
Editorial Board
E. Royalton Kisch, M.C.
Maj. Gen. R. F. B. Naylor, C.B., C.B.E., D.S.O., M.C.
Gordon Edwards, C.B.E.
L. Hollis
W. C. Thorn
Constance Wheatcroft

(Copyright Bertram Park)

Printed by
THE WHITEFRIARS PRESS LIMITED
LONDON AND TONBRIDGE
1963

LIST OF ILLUSTRATIONS

Photographs by Bertram Park and the Research Department of Boots Pure Drug Co. Ltd.

In Colour

CONTENTS

PART I

PART II

ENEMIES OF THE ROSE
by John Ramsbottom, O.B.E., M.A., Dr.Sc.

RECENT DEVELOPMENTS IN DISEASE CONTROL
by E. F. Allen

FOREWORD

This is an elementary handbook on the cultivation of roses; it is not a botanical textbook and in Part I scientific terms are kept as far as possible to a minimum.

Horticulture is not an exact science—thank goodness, and there are many ways of growing good plants. Rose-growing is no exception, but, although plenty of roses can be grown with a minimum of trouble and preparation, good flowers on good plants do require a certain amount of care and attention.

As to how much care and how much attention may be a matter of opinion, and the divergence of opinion among the " experts " frequently becomes exaggerated to positive contradictions. The recommendations in the following pages are, however, a fundamentally right way of doing those particular things. Having absorbed those recommendations the rose amateur should start to experiment for himself and, from his own experience, then find out the best methods *under his own particular conditions*.

However, whether you are able to grow, with our help, perfect flowers on perfect plants or whether your results may not be so perfect, you will find roses and rose-growing an absorbing occupation which will give you a lifelong enjoyable pursuit for pleasure.

B. P.

PART I

INTRODUCTION

*O*N *transfer from the nursery to its future home, the rose with its established root system is one of the least exacting of all horticultural products, and, given a modicum of care, there should be no casualties in transplanting apart from accident or extremes of weather. But roses even of the highest quality—and there are none finer than those produced by our British nurseries—will not thrive if they are improperly planted or they are neglected.*

A correct method of planting and the best way of dealing with unfriendly soils, with hints on general cultivation, will be found in the following pages, and close observation of the advice so given should ensure the endless pleasure and enjoyment which the rose is capable of affording.

PREPARATION OF THE SOIL

THERE are many types of soil—it may even vary from garden to garden—but the general principle of fitting it for growing roses is the same in all cases. Whatever the locality or the type of soil, the fundamental essential underlying the proper preparation of rose beds is a balance between soil aeration and moisture retention. Be it sand, silt, gravel, loam or clay, the object is to provide the plants with the nourishment they need to yield their rich harvests of bloom.

Nourishment can only be assimilated when in solution; if adequate moisture at the roots ceases, starvation begins and is soon followed by loss of vigour. To remedy this loss of vigour there may be an inclination to water the *surface* of the ground, thus inviting a too shallow root system. All goes well until one day the watering is forgotten or, having for a time enjoyed our roses in plenty, we grow tired of the job and leave the delicate root hairs of the plant just below the surface of the ground to be shrivelled by the summer sun.

Deep primary cultivation will help to provide the moisture-retaining properties of the soil below the surface and, when enriched by adequate fertilisers, both organic and chemical, will ensure a vigorous root system. Moreover, the roots need air just as much as we do, and the deep digging will enable the excess water to drain away below, drawing air in after it, for if the roots remain in waterlogged soil they will assuredly be suffocated. In addition to deep digging, therefore, some provision must be made for the surplus water to get away. To dig a small area deeply, leaving the surrounding soil undisturbed, may merely make a bath for the roots to "drown" in. If the soil is naturally porous there is no need to worry, but if it is impervious to water a wider area must be dug or a channel excavated with land drains set at a slight slope leading to a lower part of the garden, or even to a deep sump filled in with broken bricks, etc.

To test the porosity of the soil it is a good plan to dig a hole to the depth finally intended and fill it up with water. If in a day or so the water has all drained away then all is well, but if not then some special steps as indicated above must be taken to provide the essential drainage. On flat land with clay subsoil it may be advisable not to dig too deeply, but to raise the level of the bed some six or nine inches above its surroundings. One method of doing this, if you prefer gravel pathways to those of grass, is to take off the top spit from the pathway and add it to the bed, then fill in the paths with rubble and ashes and top up with hoggin, gravel or paving stones.

There is one very important point to remember in deep cultivation: *always keep the fertile surface soil on top and the subsoil below*. The best and most satisfactory way of preparing a rose bed by hand is that which is commonly known as " double digging." Remove from one end of the bed a section of eighteen inches and twelve inches deep, and clear out the remaining crumbs with a shovel. Wheel this to the corner of the bed diagonally opposite. Then dig up the bottom of the trench thus made and, if the subsoil is clay, thoroughly fork into it a liberal quantity of hydrated lime, three pounds or so to the square yard. The effect of this lime is both physical and chemical; it assists in breaking up and " crumbling " the clay, rendering it more porous and improving the drainage as well as liberating some nutrients which will be of benefit to the roses. This liberal liming should be kept well down in the subsoil, and is undesirable in light, sandy, gravelly or chalky soils.

Now proceed to open up the second eighteen-inch-wide strip, placing this top soil on top of the first dug-up section. Mix into it at the same time some garden compost and any chopped up turves, leaf mould or other organic humus-forming material and a liberal sprinkling of bone meal. Granulated peat is also a valuable addition. Stable or farmyard manure may also be mixed in if available, but care should be taken later on when planting time comes that the roots of plants do not come in actual contact with the manure. The addition of the chopped-up turves, granulated peat and other organic material is especially desirable to light and gravelly soils.

The crumbs of the second trench are now used for levelling up the surface of the first strip. Dig or fork up the bottom of the second section and proceed as before until the whole of the bed has been treated. The soil

7

removed at the beginning of the operation will be ready at the other end of the bed to fill up the final section.

By this method the subsoil is well broken up and the surface soil or " top spit " remains on top. This digging leaves the level of the bed several inches higher than before. In a few weeks it will settle, and the physical structure of the soil, which is temporarily deranged by the digging, will be regained; and with the subsequent consolidation which the soil receives during planting, the surface will be just high enough above the surrounding ground to assist the drainage.

When one rose tree only is to be planted, a modification of the same process can be carried out. Remove eighteen inches square and twelve inches deep of the top soil, clear out the crumbs and break up the subsoil with the fork, treating the top and subsoil as previously described.

REPLACEMENTS IN OLD ROSE BEDS

DISAPPOINTMENT is often caused by planting rose trees in old rose beds, in which they frequently fail to thrive. One of the first things is to see that the new plant has fresh soil in which to start life. To plant roses in old rose beds, filling up gaps here and there where old plants have died, is a mistake that is not infrequently made. New plants will not grow well and thrive in this old rose soil. A rose bed that has grown roses for ten years or more may be quite exhausted as far as roses are concerned; it is " rose sick," although some of the old plants will go on growing for many more years, because their extensive root systems are ever pushing forth to new areas. If there are many gaps in

8

A rose tree budded on a Rosa canina seedling stock, as received from the nursery

Plate I

*The same with the shoots pruned a little, any damaged roots trimmed and the
dead snag of the root stock cut away*

Plate II

Fork " planting mixture " into the soil under the roots, place the plant on a little hillock and spread the roots evenly all round. Keep the " crown " level with the surface of the bed

Plate III

Cover the roots with soil and some " planting mixture." The soil must be moist and friable, never wet

The roots in these photographs have been whitened so that they can be seen against the dark background

Plate IV

Tread lightly, taking care not to press the plant down any lower into the ground

Plate V

Finish off with loose soil level with the surrounding bed

Plate VI

this old rose bed, it is far better to take up the best of the old plants, discard the poor ones and make a new bed in fresh soil which has not grown roses for a number of years. The old bed should then be used for other crops, or, better still, put to " green manuring " for one or two years. If this is impossible and the site cannot be spared or is the only one available, then it is advisable to take out for each new plant *at least* twelve inches deep and eighteen inches square of the old soil and exchange it for soil from another part of the garden which has not previously grown roses.

PLANTING

THROUGH absence of simple precautions, many freshly planted roses fail to adjust themselves to their new surroundings as quickly as they should, despite the fact that they have been purchased from a well-known rose nurseryman. It must be remembered that a rose tree or any other plant, when removed from the nursery and sent to the purchaser, is as it were for the time being a " hospital case," and in spite of all the care bestowed upon its lifting and packing it should be so regarded. It is not suggested that the plants are hovering between life and death, but some shock from the mutilation and exposure of the roots is inevitable, and there are limits to the time during which the roots may be out of their natural element.

The best months for transplanting roses are October and early November, before the earth is chilled by the autumn rains, or in March after the frosts, but with care and suitable weather conditions it may be safely carried out at any time during the winter and after the end of March. Planting should not be carried out when there is frost in the ground or snow on the surface.

In the event of packages of rose trees being received during frosty weather, they should be left intact as received and placed in a cellar or frost-proof building until the advent of more suitable weather for planting. Covered with sacking and kept moist, the plants in their original packing, provided they are not subjected to undue exposure, will sustain no injury if left for a fortnight or so. If taken indoors it is most important that the package is kept cool and moist and to see that the plants do not dry out. Apart from this eventuality the package should be unpacked as soon as it is received from the nursery and sprinkled with water. All the foliage should have been removed at the nursery before the trees were packed, but if this has not been done the first thing to do is to cut off all the leaves with a knife or scissors at the base of the leaf stalk. This is to prevent transpiration of any more moisture through the leaves, which would cause shrivelling of the stems. If the stems are found to be somewhat shrivelled already the whole plant should be plunged into water, where it can be left up to about twenty-four hours if necessary; this will usually cause the stems to plump up again.

Sometimes the nursery may not have cut away the dead stump of the root stock protruding above the union with the scion, and this should now be cut away with sharp pruners, but be careful not to cut into the green wood of the scion rose. Soft and unripe wood should also be cut back; these are the shoots which have begun to grow in the autumn, and they would almost certainly be killed by the winter frosts.

The rose trees are now ready for planting, but if, as is often the case, wet weather has rendered the soil unworkable and unfit, a shallow trench should be opened up in some sheltered part of the garden into which the plants may be laid with the roots covered with soil and the stems partly so. They may be left thus without harm until the conditions improve; it is important not to attempt planting if the soil is wet and sticky. It must be moist and friable only.

The actual operation of planting is simple in the extreme. First obtain some granulated peat, moisten it and take a three-gallon pailful, which is sufficient for a number of trees. Mix into this about a double handful of " meat and bone meal " (but failing this then raw bone meal) to form a planting mixture. Then open a hole in the prepared ground about twelve inches or so across, wide enough to take the roots full length and of just sufficient depth so that the union of the stock and scion may be level with the surrounding soil when the planting is finished. Mix thoroughly into the soil in the hole a double handful of the " planting mixture " and draw the mixed soil up into a low hillock in the centre. Rest the crown of the plant on this, spreading out the roots equally all round, seeing that they do not cross one another. Cover the roots with planting mixture and soil, and if the soil is of a heavy nature a little sand will also help to encourage the formation of new roots. Then replace some of the soil removed when making the hole and tread *lightly*. The crown of the plant must be kept level with the surrounding ground and must not be trodden lower; if the outside of the circle be trodden first, this will keep the centre up to the required level. Then replace the remainder of the soil and leave loose, level it off and the rose tree is planted. It should be noted that if you first begin to tread round the circumference of the hole it will consolidate the soil in the middle and keep the rose tree at the correct level, but if you tread in the middle this will lower it in the soil. It must be emphasised again that the ground must be only just in moist condition; to tread it when it is really wet would be highly injurious, and in any case treading should not be overdone; on heavy land especially, it should be trodden only just sufficiently to consolidate the soil.

When all is finished the union of the stock should, as mentioned before, be level with the surface; in subsequent years the annual mulching and manuring will gradually raise the surrounding soil, so that it is unwise to plant too deeply in the first place.

Standards should be planted at the same depth as described for the bush roses, and the stake should be inserted first and the tree placed close up to it so as not to cut through the roots, which would be likely to occur if the stake were driven in afterwards. Standards may vary in height, but on no account must some be planted more deeply than others in order to level up the heads. Rugosa standards should be planted as shallow as possible, the uppermost roots being not more than three or four inches below the surface.

Bush roses may be planted eighteen to twenty-four inches apart according to the vigour of the variety. " Peace " and some of the extra vigorous varieties may be planted about two feet six inches to three feet apart. Standards may be planted not less than about two feet six inches apart, and climbers when trained horizontally to form a screen should be not less than six feet apart. There is some evidence that both Black Spot and Rust are encouraged by too close planting and also by use of fertilisers containing too high a proportion of nitrogen.

HINTS ON GENERAL CULTIVATION

THE initial preparation of the soil and the "meat and bone meal" added at planting time will give sufficient nutrition for a rose tree starting off on its new career, and it cannot be too strongly emphasised that the care bestowed upon it in its first year in its new home may well determine the growth of the tree and the enjoyment subsequently to be derived from it.

When roses have become well established the year after planting they should receive regular cultivation, and the treatment necessary to guard against pest and disease and adequate fertilisers to promote growth and freedom of flowering, if they are to give of their best.

After pruning is completed the trees should be given a spraying with a colloidal copper white oil emulsion or other suitable fungicide, mixed according to the maker's formula. The purpose of this is to clean up the stems from any over-wintering spores of Mildew or other disease. Black Spot disease is also carried over from one year to another on any fallen leaves or parts of leaves which may still be lying about on the ground, so that the ground should be sprayed as well although, apart from the dead leaves, the soil itself cannot become infected. Black Spot—perhaps strangely as one might think— is more likely to occur in the purer air of the open country and is rarely seen in built-up areas or in the suburbs of large towns, where the smoke emitted from domestic fires or factory chimneys, which contain a small proportion of sulphurous acid, acts as a fungicide and protects the roses from this and some other diseases.

A fungicide, captan, has been found to be very efficacious in the control of Black Spot disease. Sold under a proprietary name of Orthocide, this may be used instead of the copper white oil emulsion if desired. The two fungicides must not be mixed, however, as captan is not compatible with any form of oil.*

The rose beds should now be pricked over and tidied up—pricked over, not dug over, for the surface of the beds should never be disturbed more than an inch or two deep, otherwise the valuable roots near the surface may be damaged and the physical structure of the soil interfered with or deranged.

About mid-May when the soil is moist the annual mulch should be applied. Stable or farmyard manure is, of course, the ideal mulch, but nowadays this is seldom readily available and garden compost can take its place. However, add to the compost any manure that can be obtained and also a generous proportion of granulated peat, spent hops or leaf mould. Peat is of no actual manurial worth but is a most valuable soil conditioner, lightening heavy soils and making them more porous and workable and giving moisture-retaining properties to light sandy or gravelly soils, while in chalky soil it helps to neutralise the alkalinity. It is slowly converted into the humus so essential in all soil for growing plants.

During the summer months the lawn mowings may also be lightly scattered over the beds, but not thickly at one time or they will form a " blanket " not easily absorbed, but light and frequent dressings quickly become part of the soil. Granulated peat may be preferable for use as a mulch if there are seeds from annual Poa grass, which can be become a nuisance. The mulch will largely control the growth of weeds, but not entirely. During a wet summer especially the weeds are bound to make their appearance in the rich soil of the rose beds, and the flat arrow-head shaped, the push-and-pull type, or the " sproughton " type hoe is the best tool to use. This can be pushed and pulled just beneath the surface of the soil to cut the weeds, and it will disturb the mulch as

*See page 72.

14

little as possible. Hoeing should be for the destruction of weeds; the old idea that to " keep the hoe going " conserves moisture in the soil is partly true, as weeds take food from the soil and account for loss of moisture by transpiration. Hoeing will not enable " air," i.e. oxygen, to reach the roots, that is provided for by rainfall or watering as previously described. The conservation of soil water is much more efficiently performed by the addition of the annual mulch of organic material, which will prevent the moisture from evaporating. If under any circumstances the surface mulch of organic material cannot be applied, then it is important in dry weather to hoe up the surface of the soil to prevent cracking and provide an artificial mulch of dust or loose soil.

In the autumn the beds may be lightly pricked over to a depth of two or three inches, burying and tidying up what remains of the mulch. Manure should *not* be applied during the winter; the time for that is in the spring, after pruning and the first spraying.

FERTILISERS

IT is sometimes said that roses are " gross feeders "; this is an exaggeration, but they will be greatly improved—as indeed will most plants—by suitable applications of fertilisers. The first dressing of fertiliser should take the form of " meat and bone meal," of which two handfuls to the square yard should be scattered over the beds at any time in the early spring before the mulch is applied. This is a slow-acting fertiliser which provides phosphorus and a small proportion of nitrogen, but being organic it is also a valuable soil conditioner and becomes available slowly over a long period. There are various compounded or ready-made fertilisers on the market, but some have probably not been prescribed for the special requirements of the rose, and it is specially desirable to avoid any that may contain " Muriate of Potash." The packages of all mixed fertilisers are bound to indicate the *percentages* of the three principal plant nutrients—namely, nitrogen, phosphorus and potassium —but for particular plants, such as for instance the rose, it is also very important to know the salts in which the nutrients are provided, and roses do not like " Muriate of Potash " (i.e. containing commercial potassium chloride). The potassium should be supplied by sulphate of potash.

The next application should be in May and for those who may desire to mix up their own fertiliser here is one devised to meet the special requirements of the rose:

Nitrate of potash	. .	6 parts by weight
Sulphate of ammonia	. .	3 parts
Superphosphate .	. .	16 parts
Sulphate of potash	. .	8 parts
Sulphate of magnesium.	.	2 parts
Sulphate of iron .	. .	$\frac{1}{2}$ part

On chalky soils the magnesium and iron should be doubled, and on heavy clay soil if 6 parts of sulphate of calcium (gypsum) be added it will help to get the soil into better condition.

An alternative formula which has proved satisfactory on some chalk-free or acid soils:

Nitro chalk.	. .	10 parts by weight
Superphosphate .	. .	12 parts
Sulphate of potash	. .	9 parts
Sulphate of magnesium	.	2 parts
Sulphate or iron .	. .	$\frac{1}{2}$ part

Either of the above formulas can be mixed thoroughly and scattered over the surface of the beds at the rate of about two ounces or approximately a handful to the square yard, once in mid-May and once in mid-June, watering it well in afterwards.

People are sometimes heard to say that they cannot grow roses, their soil is too light and sandy. This is quite a mistaken idea; the soil in one well-known rose garden, giving a glorious display of bloom every year, was ten years previously but poor grassland and the soil mostly silt sand with a thin covering of " top spit." Roses will grow anywhere (within reason) and on any soil provided it is properly prepared and manured, but they do best in a soil which is slightly acid, having on test a reaction of pH 5·6 to 6·5. Care must always be taken therefore not to use too much lime. Certainly it helps to condition heavy land, but it is better for this purpose to use the form of calcium sulphate (gypsum).

Ground chalk (calcium carbonate) may be used in a light dressing if the soil when tested is found to be too acid, but fresh hydrated lime is not so desirable except to help in breaking up the subsoil of heavy clay land as previously described. The bone meal previously referred to and the superphosphate will also provide the calcium required in the growth of the plant.

An additional feeding through the leaves with very dilute sprays is a technique which can be very useful to encourage good foliage and so promote better growth. A dilute solution of two parts by weight of urea and one part of potassium acid phosphate (KH_2PO_4) may be used at the rate of half an ounce to the gallon of water for the purpose. There are also proprietary preparations which contain the minor elements in addition and they have been found to be particularly effective. These solutions must be made up as required as they will not keep for long in solution, and they should preferably be used in the very early morning.

There are valuable articles on fertilisers for roses on difficult soils in the Rose Annuals of 1954 and 1961, which may be consulted for further information.

PESTS AND DISEASES

AS soon as the leaves begin to open in April-May the war against the pests begins. The one most usually talked about is green-fly, but there are others that can do far more harm. A good all-purpose pest control is DDT,* except for green-fly, and it is most easily applied in the form of a powder. There are simple and inexpensive dusters or blowers readily available with which the powder can quickly and effectively be dispersed like a cloud (choose a calm day for the purpose), which drifts on to every part of the foliage. This will deal with all the caterpillars and maggots but, unfortunately, will not control green-fly, which must be dealt with by a separate spray. There are many efficient proprietary preparations: Pyrethex, Sybol, Lindane, Malathion or Derris solutions, diluted to the strength prescribed by the manufacturers, can be used with the ordinary garden sprayer for this purpose and will soon clear up the trouble. Malathion is a multi-purpose insecticide which has been found to be particularly effective against green-fly and many other pests.

Mildew on the foliage of some varieties is disfiguring and will spoil the appearance of any rose bed. An attack is often favoured by cold nights after hot days, and is therefore usually more prevalent in the early autumn than in high summer. A colloidal copper oil emulsion spray affords an immediate cure, and is the same spray which may be used in spring after the completion of the pruning. This spray is also suitable if there should be any trouble with Rust disease.

Captan (Orthocide) is most effective against Black Spot but is not compatible with any oil spray so must not

*Use with care, D.D.T. is dangerous to bees.

be used if the copper emulsion is preferred. For Mildew another preparation is Karathane and a combined mixture in water at a strength given in the maker's instructions of Orthocide and Karathane will effectively deal with both these troubles. Neither of these preparations are suitable for controlling Rust disease and if they are used in preference to a copper emulsion then another would have to be used for Rust. For this purpose thiram has been found to be effective. It may be combined with the other two if required, but it is comparatively rarely that Rust and Black Spot occur at the same time. The newer materials zineb and maneb are referred to on page 73.

It should, however, be understood that while Mildew can be to a large extent " cured ", the spraying recommended for Black Spot and Rust is preventive and a protectant, and should be used accordingly at the first signs of trouble in order to prevent further infection.

If these diseases should be prevalent in the neighbourhood or plants have suffered from them previously, it is well to take the precaution of giving a regular spraying with the appropriate mixtures once every fortnight (or every ten days if the trouble has been bad) from July onwards. A warning must, however, be given here. When plants are in poor health or growing in poor soil and are semi-starved, they may show symptoms of nutritional deficiency by poor growth and often by markings on the foliage known as " Purple Spotting." This is not Black Spot, but plants in this unhealthy condition are liable to damage by *any* spraying with full-strength mixtures. In this case it may be advisable at first to use the copper oil emulsion or other sprays mentioned at half the strength given in the maker's instructions, to avoid any possible damage to foliage which might arise from their use. Some damage has been reported from some districts when the plants were not growing strongly. Under these conditions the first thing to do is to see that the plants are growing properly again by cultivation of the soil and the incorporation of adequate humus-forming material: dung, garden compost, lawn mowings and granulated peat, and the provision of sufficient fertilisers.

In the early summer the young foliage may sometimes be damaged by a slight night frost or cold winds, and then may show brown or purplish markings and have a shrivelled appearance. This again is not a disease but only the effects of the weather, and the plants will grow out of it as more favourable weather comes. Spraying with clean water will help the plants, but there should be no spraying with fungicides. In urban or built-up areas roses are rarely troubled with disease except that of Mildew because, as said before, the minute proportions of sulphurous acid emitted by domestic and factory chimneys is sufficient to protect them.

Chlorosis is a deficiency symptom which frequently occurs when the plants are growing in areas with a chalky subsoil. It is shown by the leaves turning yellow in parts or in extreme cases the whole of the leaves may lose their rich green colouring. Owing to the excess of lime the leaves are unable to take up sufficient iron and other salts from the soil. It may help if the soil is watered with a solution of sulphates or iron and magnesium (Epsom salts), but it is much more effective if the iron salt is applied in a chelated form such as Iron Sequestrene or Sequestrene Plus. Either should be watered in or sprayed, using a mild detergent as a spreader, according to the maker's instructions. Every endeavour should also be made to render the soil more acid by ample manuring with old strawy dung from stables or by the addition of other humus-forming material which helps to neutralise the alkaline soil. It will also help to give a dressing of two ounces of flowers of sulphur to the square yard and to keep a good mulch of peat, two or three inches deep, spread over the surface. In poor soil and under drought conditions and in the autumn some of the foliage may turn yellow; this is not lime chlorosis but indicates a weakening of the growth of the plant.

There follows in Part II more extensive scientific descriptions of the pests and diseases to which the rose is subject. The " Enemies of the Rose " handbook of the Society gives a full description of all pests and diseases which are likely to give trouble in the rose garden; this may be borrowed from the library and members are referred to it for further information.

On page 71 will be found notes on recent developments in disease control, an addition to this 1963 Edition, by E. F. Allen.

PROPAGATION

TAKING CUTTINGS

MANY varieties of more vigorous character, the ramblers in particular, can be propagated by cuttings, and by so doing plants are obtained on their own roots; as to whether this is an advantage or not is a matter of opinion. It is not always the best way of getting good plants, as the roots of the wild species upon which the cultivated varieties are usually budded are more extensive and more vigorous.

Yellow varieties do not strike well, but to take cuttings of red and pink varieties choose well-ripened shoots of first summer's growth, about ten inches long, in November and make a clean cut immediately below the lowest eye. To do this it is best to cut first with the secateurs about a quarter inch lower than the eye and then to trim it up to the right place with a sharp knife. The upper end of the cutting should be trimmed above an eye with a slanting cut as in pruning and it is better to leave two or three leaves if possible. Take out a trench about six inches deep and place along the bottom, three inches deep, a mixture of half sharp sand and half well-moistened granulated moss peat. Place the cuttings about four inches apart in this so that one-third of the cutting protrudes above the surface of the soil, and tread the ground well. Rooting will be assisted by placing cloches over the row of cuttings. There are certain hormone root-promoting substances both in liquid and in powder form which will certainly assist in the formation of roots. The cuttings are placed in a weak solution of this chemical before being planted out; with the powder form the cuttings are wetted and just dipped in the powder. In both cases the maker's instructions should be followed exactly.

The cuttings should remain undisturbed for a year and lifted the following autumn. Some will have rooted and may then be planted out in their beds. By this means you *may* have flowering plants in two or three years. By budding, however, first-class flowering plants can be produced twelve months after the bud, or eye, is inserted in the stock.

BUDDING

SOONER or later every keen rosarian will want to try his hand at budding his own plants. This does not mean that he becomes a less valuable customer to his nurseryman; on the contrary, the rose lover who is sufficiently interested to master the craft of budding will always want to increase his collection.

Budding is a simple operation, and if carried out in the right manner need present no insuperable difficulties which any amateur gardener cannot successfully undertake. The first consideration is the provision of suitable stocks, and these should be selected according to the conditions in your garden. A great deal has been said about the compatibility of the stock with the scion variety, but it is far more important to have the stocks suitable to the soil and climate. For instance, in most parts of North America the *Rosa multiflora* stock is used; in France multiflora or canina are used in the north and middle region, and R. *odorata* in the warm and dry climate of the south. These and other varieties are used in other countries according to the prevailing conditions.

In England the most popular understock is the canina seedling, and if a good variety is obtained this is the best stock for heavy and average soils, but these seedlings are often a mixed lot and a number of sub-varieties may appear, making for unequal growth and " take." Moreover, some of the varieties throw up suckers from the roots even more readily than rugosa, which is a stock usually avoided for dwarf bushes on that account. The so-called R. *laxa* stock, which is actually a sub-species of canina and is said to be a hybrid of R. *alba* and R. *canina*, is extremely even and regular, and under good conditions it gives an exceptionally high " take "; it gives vigorous and healthy plants and very rarely is it known to throw suckers. Its only drawback is that it matures early in the season as the sap does not " run " well later in the summer. There are also a number of other selected sub-species of canina, of which Polmeriana is one of the best.

On poor sandy soil there is no doubt that R. *multiflora* gives the best results, and the thorned variety (having prickles singly up the stems and in pairs at the base of the leaf stalks, red when young and black when ripe) is the hardiest and the best. It is sometimes called in the trade " polyantha simplex," or just " simplex." In September cuttings are taken of the current year's growth about ten inches long, of which the lower cut is just below an eye and the upper cut just above an eye, and the three lowest eyes are cut out and the cuttings are inserted two inches apart in sandy soil to root. These will have calloused and rooted enough by the following March to lift and plant in the nursery beds for budding in July and August. Canina (briar) cuttings may be taken in a similar manner, but with these it is advisable to use a hormone powder

The stem with leaves and thorns trimmed

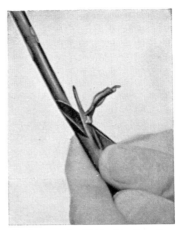

Cutting out the shield with the embryo " eye " or " bud "

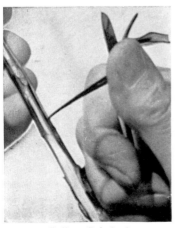

Pulling off the bark

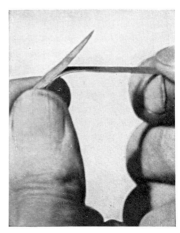

Pulling the bark down from the wood

Plate VII

Separating the wood

The back of the shield, showing the embryo bud or eye

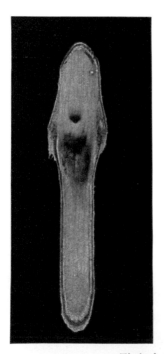

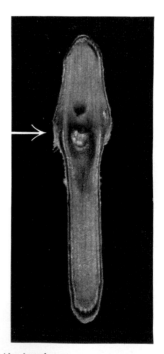

The back of the shield enlarged
Left: *Showing the growth torn out*
Right: *The growth as it should be, flush with the shield*
Plate VIII

The cut in the lateral of a standard

The shield tied in

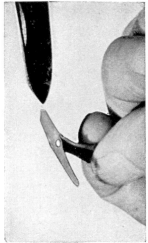

The shield trimmed

The shield inserted and the overlapping piece of bark cut off

Plate IX

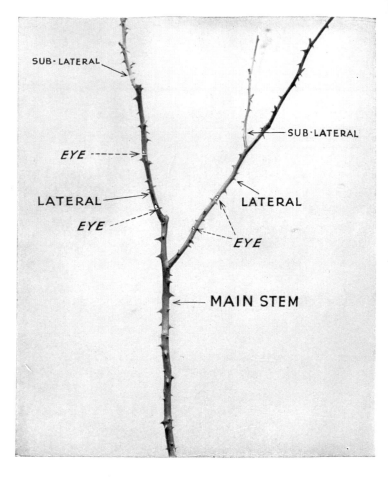

"EYES" AND "LATERALS"

These terms are frequently used throughout this handbook and may require explanation. As will be seen by the above illustration, by an " Eye " is meant a **bud** *on the main stem or any of the other shoots. By a " Lateral " is meant a* **side shoot** *on any leading branch or shoot. By a " Sub-Lateral " is meant a shoot issuing from a Lateral*

Plate X

root-promoting preparation, as otherwise they are much more difficult to strike successfully and they have to remain for a whole year to root before being taken up to plant out.

It is often said that roses budded on cutting stocks have not such a long life as those budded on seedling stocks, and, if desired, your usual nurseryman will no doubt be willing to supply you with some suitable seedling stocks. There are some nurserymen who make a speciality of growing and supplying them. These may be planted in early spring, preferably in a separate plot in the garden, whence they should be transplanted in the autumn following their first flowering. It is not wise to plant the stocks in the beds where they are to remain permanently, as even in the unlikely event of a 100 per cent take there are certain to be some inferior plants which will make for inequalities in the bed. Also the roots will be penetrating too deeply, whereas by transplanting and thus trimming the roots these will be kept nearer the surface, which is the better place for them. On the other hand, many exhibitors prefer to bud their stocks *in situ* where they are to remain. This is one of those cases where amateurs should experiment for themselves and find out the methods which suit them best under their own conditions.

Plant the stocks about ten inches apart and two feet six inches between the rows. If they are seedlings keep the neck, i.e. the part between the root where it forks out and the green shoots above, an inch or so above the level of the ground for convenience in budding later when the time comes. If they are rooted cuttings, plant the roots as shallow as possible, and both sorts are more conveniently worked if set at a slight slope to the ground. Dry weather in July or August sometimes causes the canina or laxa temporarily to cease growing, and it is then useless to try and bud them. One must wait for rain or give a copious watering with the hose to start them off again, when they can be worked in a few days. The multiflora stocks stand dry weather better, but in very wet weather they are inclined to grow too vigorously; they may be restrained by trimming back some of the shoots. A stock which grows to much more than half an inch in diameter may give unsatisfactory results in that it may "drown" the bud, and the cut of the heading back will heal over with difficulty and remain open to infection with disease.

Stocks planted in March should be ready for budding in July or August. A good-quality knife should be procured of which the other end to the blade is thin and wedge-shaped for the purpose of lifting the bark. The blade must be stropped to a razor sharpness on a leather strop or fine emery-paper stick. Having chosen the variety to be propagated, select a shoot when the flower is just fading and before the prickles have dried and hardened; the leaves are trimmed off, leaving about half an inch of the leaf stalk by which to hold the shield. Have some good raffia cut to a length of about twenty-two inches and stripped to a width of about one-third of an inch. Patches of rubber fastened with a staple or strips of rubber are also frequently used. The advantage of these is that they stretch with the growth of the stock and do not tend to strangle it.

The professional budder will work down the rows of stocks in a standing position with expert speed, doing many hundreds a day, but some of us may be stiff in the joints and, though it may be slower, it is easier to work with one knee on the ground—softened maybe with a rubber kneeling pad—and the other foot thrown forward to balance the weight of the body. A flat stick or trowel scrapes away the soil from the base of the stock, and a rag cleans away any dirt on the stem. The whole job must be kept as clean as possible; it is really a surgical operation.

A cross-cut is first made in the neck of the stock, one inch above the forking of the roots and a quarter inch wide and just deep enough to penetrate the bark, but no more; then, starting about three-quarters of an inch below, make the upright cut to meet the other in a T shape. At the finish of this cut give the knife a slight twist on either side to lift the corner of the bark, then reverse the knife and with the other end lift up the bark as shown in the illustration. Now without delay take the shoot with the eyes to be used as scions, snap off the prickles and commence to cut the lowest eye; cut down the stem under the eye to about half an inch below, then close down the thumb on to the shield and pull off the strip of bark, change the shield to the other hand and pull down the strip of bark to loosen the piece of wood under the eye; take hold of this piece of wood and snatch it out with a slight twisting movement. All that now remains is to trim up the shield and it is ready for insertion into the cut in the stock; finally tie in firmly with the rubber over the bud, or if raffia is used take two turns below the bud and three above. All this takes long to describe and may not be easy to follow, but the illustrations should make the whole operation perfectly clear.

Briar standards are budded in exactly the same way, but the eyes are inserted in the laterals, as close to the main stem as possible, and two or three laterals are used. Rugosa standards are budded in the main stem, and again two or three are usually put in on opposite sides of the stem. The raffia ties on the standards must be cut after about a month, but those on the dwarf stocks may be earthed up with a shallow covering of soil and will then rot off during the winter. The rubber strips require no further attention.

The next stage is the heading back early the next year, in January or February, when the weather is dry and free from frost. If necessary one must postpone operations until the weather conditions are suitable, but it is not desirable to wait until the sap is rising, as then much bleeding will occur. Try and cut the stock back as high on the neck as possible; some may have already grown out, and it is not advisable to cut into the green wood of the shield. With cuttings one inch is right, but with seedling stocks there may not be an inch to leave, so cut as high as possible. This piece of the stock above the eye will die back in due course and should be trimmed off when the plant is eventually transplanted. If the cutting back is done too close to the eye, this is where the infection from that dread disease canker (*Conio-thyrium*) frequently occurs. If there are old plants in the garden or the same soil has been used before for growing roses then it is desirable to paint the heading back with some disinfectant. Copper oil emulsion in its concentrated form, straight out of the bottle, on a stiff paint brush is satisfactory for the purpose.

Roses budded on to multiflora stock make a very insecure joint the first season, and the new growths should be staked with a cane, tying them first when they are nine inches long. With other stocks it is not so essential, but to avoid risk of loss through breaking out it is just as well also to tie the new growths to a short cane; on standards they should all be tied. The new plants will flower from June onwards and in late October should be lifted and transferred to their permanent quarters.

THE CLASSIFICATION OF ROSES
FOR GARDEN PURPOSES

IN times past it was the custom to separate garden roses into various classes according to their pedigree, but in recent years this has become increasingly difficult, as the types of the Hybrid Tea and the Hybrid Polyantha in particular have begun to merge. There are now roses of Hybrid Polyantha pedigree which have all the characteristics of the Hybrid Tea, so much so that it would be misleading to place them anywhere but with the latter. The hybridists are now using many different species in the raising of varieties similar to those which were known as Hybrid Polyanthas, so that they can no longer be correctly included in that description.

It is therefore now more convenient to group roses for garden purposes according to their appearance rather than to their parentage, and those in the " Roses: a Selected List " handbook of the National Rose Society are divided as follows :—

The Hybrid Tea Type. Herein are included all Hybrid Tea, Hybrid Perpetual, Pernetiana, Tea and large flowered roses of similar character to that which is now recognised as a Hybrid Tea.

There are very few varieties of the originally distinct classes of Tea, Hybrid Perpetual or Pernetiana roses in cultivation. Nearly all modern roses of the Hybrid Tea type have some strain of *Rosa fœtida* in their pedigree, though it is more evident in those of yellow, orange or flame shades, but that strain has gradually become recessive to other strains continuously introduced, so that there is no object in perpetuating the term Pernetiana.

The Floribunda Bedding Roses include those varieties

which bear their flowers in large trusses or clusters, in which many open at the same time, and on plants which normally grow to a height suitable for bedding purposes.

There are a few modern varieties which in their appearance may be on the border line between these two classes and these are described here and in " The Selected List" as *Floribunda—hybrid tea type*.* If disbudded to a single flower on a stem these will give a moderate sized hybrid tea type bloom, but otherwise will flower in clusters as is their normal habit and that generally of the floribunda class.

The Floribunda Shrub Roses include varieties of similar flowering habit to the previous class, but which normally grow too tall for bedding purposes and are more suitable for planting as individual specimen bushes, or in the shrub border and for hedges.

The Polyantha Pompons (the dwarf growing cluster Roses), the *Ramblers*, *Climbers* and the *Miniature China Roses* remain classified as previously.

* Some of these have been called—" *Grandiflora*" in America, which is a totally misleading description.

INTRODUCTION TO PRUNING

THE late Reverend A. Foster-Melliar in his "Book of the Rose" pointed out that the necessity for pruning arises in a great measure from the natural growth of the Rose. "By watching," he said, "an unpruned Rose tree, either wild or cultivated, it will be found that the first strong shoot flowers well the second season, but gets weaker at the extremity in a year or two, and another strong shoot starts considerably lower down, or even from the very base of the plant, and this soon absorbs the majority of the sap, and will eventually starve the original shoot and be itself thus starved in succession by another. A Rose in a natural state has thus every year some branches which are becoming weakened by the fresh young shoots growing out below them. This is one of the principal reasons why pruning is necessary. A Rose is not a tree to grow onwards and upwards, but a plant which in the natural course every year or two forms fresh channels for the major portion of the sap, and thus causes the branches and twigs above the new shoots to diminish in vitality."

From this it may be gathered that nature's method of getting rid of the undesirable parts of the plant is the slow one of gradual starvation; and it is wasteful, in that during the process even the strong shoots are likely to become weakened, injured or diseased.

The rosarian's aim is to have healthy, well-formed plants; and from them to obtain either a small number of large perfect blooms or a greater number of usually smaller ones. To achieve this he must prune. The art of pruning is the cutting away of those parts of the plant which the study of nature has shown to be useless for producing the best results, thus throwing the whole strength of the plant into the most satisfactory shoots.

PRUNING THE HYBRID TEA TYPE ROSES

Maidens, i.e. *first year plants,* require to be pruned fairly severely—each stem cut back to about six inches from the ground to an eye pointing outwards from the centre. The reason for this is to increase the number of shoots from low down on the plant in order to build up a bushy, well-balanced tree. Stems left long pruned in this first year tend only to send out new growths from the topmost eyes with the result that the trees become leggy and unsightly. The only exception to initial hard pruning is when the trees are planted in very poor or sandy soils; experience has shown it is best to leave the harder pruning until the second year in order to allow the plant first to become established.

After the first year pruning has an important part to play in the continued health of the bush. We in our own lives know the simple rules of hygiene which demand light and air for our healthy development; as with human beings, so with the living plant. A bush Hybrid Tea Type rose left to itself will develop a large number of shoots which in increasing competition for light and air will become thin, spindly and the breeding place of all the evils of neglected plants. Overcrowding of the shoots will lead to the breeding of disease with premature defoliation, and will encourage all the pests of the rose world.

A rose branch showing the position of the " eyes "

Plate XI

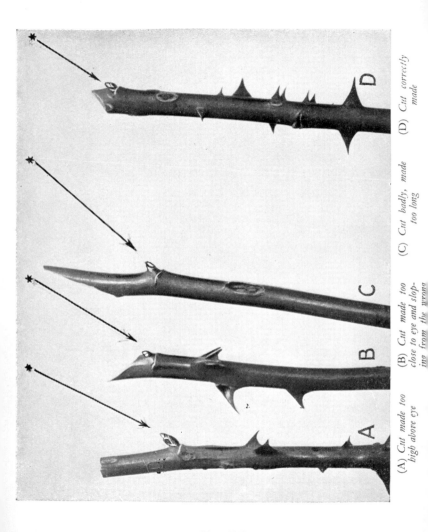

(A) *Cut made too high above eye* (B) *Cut made too close to eye and sloping from the wrong* (C) *Cut badly, made too long* (D) *Cut correctly made*

Plate XII

A MAIDEN HYBRID TEA PLANT

As planted   *Pruned*

This plant has been left too long before being pruned and new spring growth has already commenced

Plate XIII

Crimson Glory
Hybrid Tea Type
Moderate to light pruning recommended

Plate XV

-Opposite page (Plate XIV) **Crimson Glory** *Hybrid Tea Type*

Hector Deane

Hybrid Tea Type
Moderately pruned
If more lightly pruned and well cultivated, it will make a big specimen bush

Plate XVII

osite page (Plate XVI) **Hector Deane** *Hybrid Tea Type*

DAINTY MAID

Untormed

Plate XVIII

Always try to make an open cup-shaped bush so that light and air may reach the centre and circulate freely through all the branches. For this reason, when pruning, cut to an eye that points outwards. This may mean having to sacrifice two or three eyes before finding a healthy one pointing in the right direction.

With the above points in mind, it is obvious that the first task on approaching a bush for pruning will be to remove all dead and weak twiggy growth, decadent wood that did not throw out a good shoot from last year's pruning cut, and then all shoots damaged by gale, pest or disease. This task being finished, turn to pruning the healthy growths, and for the average rose variety in the average garden *moderate* pruning will give the best results. *Moderate pruning* may be briefly described as reducing both new basal shoots and ripe laterals from old wood to about half the length of the previous year's growth. Soft young shoots which have started to grow from the base after the end of August are not likely to be ripened and they should be cut right back in the autumn, or when first noticed.

Preferably prune to a healthy, plump but dormant eye; although an eye which has begun to grow out may have to be left if the pruning has been too long delayed. It is important that the wood is cut so that the eye is not damaged, and the open wound encouraged to heal as quickly as possible. To bring about this rapid healing the cut should be clean and sloping, with the lowest point of the slope behind the shoot (on the opposite side to the eye) and the highest point about a quarter-inch above the top of the eye. One of the causes of losses among rose trees is the rough cutting and bruising of the shoot during pruning. Nothing is better than a good quality slightly hooked knife, and providing the cutting begins at the bottom of the blade and is completed by drawing the whole blade across the shoot, completing the severance at the point, it is both quick and easy. Failing this, a good pair of pruning shears should be used, leaving a little more wood above the eye than with the knife pruning. *Keep the tools clean and sharp;* a dirty knife or pruning shears can carry disease infection from one plant to another.

Moderate pruning holds good for the majority of Hybrid Tea Type roses during their long life, bearing a few facts in mind. In a first-year bush, pruning to the third or fourth good eye leaves the stems about six inches high. The second year, pruning to about half the length of the previous year's growth leaves the bush proportionately higher, and so each year the bush increases in girth and height. So far so good, but with increasing age other problems arise. The older shoots may deteriorate, and to stimulate growth from the base it is occasionally advisable to cut one of the older shoots back to a dormant eye, within a few inches of the base. By so doing from time to time new growth will be encouraged from the base of the plant, thus, over a period, rejuvenating the whole bush.

One of the reasons for pruning roses is the necessity demanded by the more artificial and circumscribed limits of the average garden. If one has a bed of roses all of one variety, it is obviously unwise to treat each one as an individual specimen. The plants need to have some uniformity of height to give the bed the even growth which so enhances the mass effect. Similarly, if these Hybrid Tea Type roses are grown as specimen bushes, much lighter pruning may be indicated, not forgetting, however, the desirability of occasionally cutting a shoot back to induce fresh growth from the base in order to furnish the lower part of the plant with new shoots, foliage and flower. There are many problems which face the novice, for roses cannot be regimented into exact categories, obeying unvarying rules. Hence the necessity for observation and experiment. A weak variety on poor soil with little nourishment may become a strong grower under ideal conditions for nourishment and environment. Thus light pruning on well prepared fertile soil under good conditions may yield excellent results which could not be expected in some other gardens.

A type of growth which often bewilders is seen in some vigorous modern varieties which will often produce three shoots from one eye and when this happens the two surplus shoots should be rubbed out when they start to grow. *Never let more than one shoot grow from a pruning cut.* If, however, they should be overlooked then during the summer or at next pruning time the centre shoot of the three should be cut right out. With the outer shoots pruned lightly a better effect will thus be obtained.

The normal TIME FOR PRUNING should be *when the plants are dormant*, i.e. at any time after leaf fall in the winter, and those varieties which tend to retain their foliage may be pruned at the same time as those which have shed their leaves. All pruning should preferably be finished before the sap is rising and new growth has started in the spring. A pruned plant will not be more damaged by frost than one that has not been pruned. The young shoots of a plant pruned early and which have " grown with the weather," will be well developed and may be in a better condition to withstand the effects of a May frost, should it occur, than those on a plant which was pruned in late March or April.

Standards. The pruning of standards both of the Hybrid Tea Type and Floribunda differs in no respect from the general instructions given in the foregoing pages, except that with most varieties *moderate* pruning will be found to give the best results.

Pruning for Exhibition. The foregoing remarks apply also, in their essentials, to pruning for exhibition purposes, but here the object in view is totally different; the production of high quality specimen blooms on a given date. Every variety in a normal season takes its own time from the date of the pruning to the perfect flower. The difference may be from ten and a half weeks (" Picture ") to sixteen weeks in some varieties, then, if the date of the Show is at the end of June the date for pruning can be calculated by experience according to the locality. The method adopted by the majority of exhibitors is to prune hard each year to three or four eyes from the base of the plant, thus limiting the number of shoots and disbudded blooms. On the other hand, some exhibitors find by encouraging the plants to grow into big bushes by moderate pruning (as previously defined) and then limiting the number of shoots and blooms to develop, that equally good and sometimes better results are obtained. It is often the biggest plants which give the biggest blooms.

Summer " Pruning." Cutting flowers in the summer is a form of summer pruning, and it is possible to help or hinder a bush in its development by the length of stem which is cut with the blooms during the flowering period. If a succession of long stems is cut from the bush at the peak period of growth, the plant must suffer. The growing plant needs the food produced by the leaves and stored in the stems. To prune a growing shoot harder than one prunes a dormant tree is surely to make for rapid deterioration. A healthy plant will not suffer unduly if some of its shoots are taken, but if every

36

flower is cut with a long stem then the health of the plant will suffer and the life of the tree will be short. Never cut a flower stem longer than is really required. If two flower stems are competing for a confined space, take one but leave the other; the remaining shoot will develop fully and ripen for next year's blooms. Always look to the future; when cutting that choice bloom an extra inch or two left on the bush may leave an eye pointing outwards and thus maintain the symmetry of the bush which otherwise might be lost.

Flowers that remain on the tree until they fade should be cut back to the second or third eye below the flower, which is pointing in the direction you wish the new shoot to grow. Summer pruning may be said to be the cutting of the blooms with a view to the next crop and that of the following season as well as that of providing decoration for the home.

In conclusion, pruning is not an abstruse science but a quite simple annual gardening job, so let experience and observation be your guide. Local factors are important, therefore discuss the matter with neighbouring rose lovers, try the methods described; but they are your own roses, which, grown by yourself, will bring endless pleasure and accumulated experience.

SUMMARY

Moderate pruning is to cut out all weak and twiggy growth and all dead and old wood which did not throw a good shoot from the previous year's pruning cut. Cut away all crossing stems and those growing towards the centre of the bush. Reduce to about half their length the ripe main and lateral growths of the previous summer, cutting to an eye pointing in the direction you wish the new shoot to grow. All the large flowered Hybrid Tea Type roses, except where specially recommended otherwise, are suitable for moderate pruning.

Light pruning to be applied to those varieties where it is specially suitable, is as above, but instead of reducing the shoot or stem to half its length, cut back only to the second or third eye immediately below the pedicels or flower-bearing foot stalks.

PRUNING THE FLORIBUNDA ROSES

It seems that the pruning of this class of roses is sometimes beset with difficulties for the average rosarian. Many gardens will show that these roses are not happy under the treatment they are receiving. This is not surprising, for floribunda roses are a very vigorous, continuous flowering type, which do not need hard pruning, yet with light pruning become a thicket of shoots after a few years.

This problem appeared in a less active form when the polyantha pompons made their way into public favour, but being less vigorous the difficulties were not so apparent. With floribundas the problem became more acute and a solution was sought by pruning some hundreds of these in different ways.

Briefly, an experiment was carried out over several years and each group was treated in the same manner from beginning to end. The group severely pruned almost died and proved by their lack of growth and flower that this method was definitely bad. Very light pruning produced big bushes, which became increasingly diseased and filled with weakly growth. Moderately light pruning produced even bushes with fair blooms both in quality and quantity, but the flowering period was shortened, as few autumn growths were thrown up and there was a tendency for older wood to die without producing new wood to take its place.

It was found that two methods of pruning were needed: (1) light pruning to produce early flowers, and (2) harder pruning to produce later blooms and to provide new growth for another season. The method evolved has proved to be thoroughly satisfactory over a period of many years.

The first spring after planting, prune moderately hard. Remove weakly shoots and cut back healthy growth to about six to nine inches from the ground, but always pruning to a healthy outward eye.

The second year consists of pruning the new one-year-old wood lightly; these are the main shoots either from the base or very near the base of the bush. If a secondary shoot or shoots have developed just below the flower head, as often happens, these are shortened to three or four eyes, the top one again pointing in an outward direction. The older wood which was pruned the previous year to three or four eyes should now have good growth from such shoots, when if fully vigorous they may be shortened to about half their length, always providing the centre of the bush is kept clear and over-crowding of the shoots prevented.

Pruning in the third and succeeding years consists of pruning one-year-old wood lightly, if healthy and from the base or near the base of the bush, and cutting the remaining older wood moderately hard. Thus, wood lightly pruned the second year is pruned moderately hard the following year.

Such pruning can go on for many years and the bush always contains a proportion of lightly pruned young growth and a small proportion of older harder pruned growth. By this method the flowering season is prolonged, the lightly pruned wood flowering earlier and the hard pruned wood throwing strong shoots, which continue to flower until late autumn. A further very important point is that old wood, which so often harbours pests and diseases, is removed and the light and air thus provided encourages healthy growth.

Treated in this manner the trees maintain their natural

height and a bed when pruned is even and produces a uniform level for its successive flower crops, giving the mass effect so needed in floribundas.

The method can be successfully extended and adapted with these roses for hedges, as specimens or as a group in the perennial border. The principle is always the same. All weakly growths cleared out; sufficient older growths cut hard back to provide basal growth; enough young shoots are left to provide early flowers and also to encourage basal growth. If more height is required, then the healthiest and most vigorous shoots can be left for a further year, lightly pruning the second-year growths. In this way a six- or eight-foot specimen can be built up, with flowers and foliage from top to bottom —a lovely sight.

It will be realised that the more vigorous floribundas, the hybrid polyanthas, the hybrid moschatas, the Pemberton and other " Hybrid Musks," hybrid rubiginosas (Sweet Briars), etc., may ultimately grow even taller than eight feet, but the same principle may be applied although it may be possible to leave an older growth for a longer period. Decreasing vigour will give warning that its useful days are over and the time for its removal has come.

PRUNING THE RAMBLERS AND CLIMBERS

There are two types of ramblers and they call for different treatment. Group 1 includes the true ramblers, hybrids of *Rosa wichuraiana* such as " Dorothy Perkins." To Group 2 belong those similar to " Paul's Scarlet " and " Chaplin's Pink," and the " Alberic Barbier " type. In Groups 3 and 4 are Climbing Hybrid Tea types and similar large flowered varieties.

Groups 1 and 2 should be pruned in early autumn as soon after the flowering season as may be convenient. Groups 3 and 4 are pruned any time in late autumn or winter, but before any new growth starts in spring; this is important, as to do this job in late spring inevitably means damage to the buds on the new shoots.

Group 1 gives the least trouble in the matter of pruning; it is simply a matter of cutting away in the early autumn the whole of the previous season's growth which has flowered, to the ground. During the summer fresh growths have started and these should be retained full length and carefully tied in. These will provide the flowers for the following year. In a dry season if the plant is not very vigorous and there is not sufficient new wood it may sometimes be advisable to retain some of the previous year's growth, cutting back all the laterals to two or three eyes. The trusses of flower will not, however, be so large as those on the new growths from the base.

Group 2 is also fairly easy to manage, except that the number of new growths from the base are fewer and sometimes absent altogether. The new growths more frequently spring from the older wood higher up the stems. The lower part of older plants sometimes gets rather bare, and in order to clothe the base and induce new growth lower down, one or two of the old stems may occasionally be cut hard to a good dormant eye a foot or eighteen inches from the base. For the rest, old wood higher up should be cut back to where a good new leading shoot has started, and where there is no new leading shoot it may be cut away entirely. These leading shoots should be retained full length and other shorter laterals all reduced back to two or three inches from where they started.

THE CLIMBERS

The climbing sports and climbers are divided into two groups. The vigorous growers suitable for walls, pergolas, hedges or for covering fences, and the moderate growers which are more suitable for training up pillars or posts, or for forming large free bushes.

Group 3. Do not prune any of the new growth unless it is damaged, and retain as much of it as possible; cut back only to keep within the allotted space. Old and exhausted wood should be cut out and the laterals trimmed to a few eyes from where they started according to their thickness. *Newly planted trees of this group must not be pruned at all the first year after planting*, as this sometimes may give such a check as to cause them to revert to the dwarf form. Every encouragement should be given by syringing with water to induce the plants to break into new growth should there be a dry period during spring.

Group 4. Moderate climbers or " pillar roses." Pruning consists here solely in cutting out dead, old or worn-out wood and keeping the plants to a good shape. Newly planted trees of this group also must not be pruned the first year.

POLYANTHA POMPONS

These are dwarf bushy plants, and all the pruning that is necessary is to cut back the old flower stems to an upper eye, and to eliminate old wood that has not given a good new shoot the previous year.

Used for bedding the plants should be kept to an even height, and may be pruned at any time when the plants are dormant. When newly planted they should not be pruned so severely as the hybrid tea type or the floribundas.

SWEET BRIARS

The Sweet Briars are early summer flowering, vigorous growers and frequently used for hedging, for which purpose they should be tied down to an open fence or other support. Most of them grow to about ten feet, and the foliage has the characteristic Sweet Briar perfume. No pruning is necessary except to cut out dead wood, and as may be necessary to keep them within their allotted space.

THE ROSE SPECIES

The species and hybrids of species need no pruning except to cut out dead wood and keep the bushes shaped up to their allotted space. In course of time some may become bare in the lower parts of the stems, "leggy," and some of the main stems may be cut back fairly hard to induce fresh growth to break and clothe the lower parts of the bush, so gradually rejuvenating the whole. See also the note on the pruning of the very vigorous floribunda roses.

WEEPING STANDARDS

WEEPING Standards are rambler roses budded at the top of tall briar or rugosa stems, but the latter are liable to throw up suckers from the roots. The pruning is carried out in the same manner as for ordinary ramblers, but with certain modifications, for owing to the length of the stems, the amount of growth produced is much less than that of ramblers budded on the stock at ground level in the usual way. The amount of growth, too, will vary greatly according to the soil conditions, and the suitability of the situation.

The No. 1 Group of Ramblers is the most satisfactory for " Weepers " as in this group the annual new growths from the crown are usually ample, and the whole of that which has flowered the previous year can be cut right out. If, however, it is found that there is insufficient, the best of the older growth may be retained, merely cutting back the flowering laterals to an inch or so from the main stems.

In Group 2, which is not so suitable for Weeping Standards although they are sometimes grown in this form, pruning should be confined to cutting out the older wood if required and reducing the laterals.

It is not recommended that wire trainers should be used; the trees look very much better if they are grown naturally with the long canes hanging down to the ground, as they will do if suitable varieties are chosen. If an extra strong growth protrudes it can easily be tied down to keep it in place.

HYBRID MUSKS AND SIMILAR
FLORIBUNDA SHRUB ROSES

The so-called " Hybrid Musks " are classified as such for their typical habit of growth, although most varieties have but a very distant relationship, if any, to the species R. *moschata*.

These are all notably free from any disease; they are suitable for specimen bushes, the shrub border and for hedging. No pruning necessary, other than to shape them up and keep to their proper space. To encourage the later flowering, the dead trusses should be cut back to the second leaf after the first flush. If plants become " leggy " in course of time, one or more of their main shoots may be cut back fairly hard to induce fresh growth from the base. See also notes on pruning the very vigorous floribunda roses.

MINIATURE CHINA ROSES

When it is desired to grow these in pots for room decoration, they should be grown on in a frame or glass house until ready to flower, when they may be brought indoors. They should be sprayed night and morning and at night taken into a cool room (if possible with a moist atmosphere). When they have finished their first flowering, they must be taken out again at once to the frame or greenhouse, where they should be grown on again. No pruning is required, merely cut out any dead wood and keep the plants in shape.

Miniature China roses should be propagated by cuttings, or division of the roots unless they have been budded. Budded or grafted plants grow much bigger and thus lose one of their most charming characteristics. The plants on their own roots are also much longer lived.

ROSES IN POTS UNDER GLASS

AFTER the spring blooming the roses in pots are stood out of doors where they have some shade during part of the day. In November they are brought under cover and allowed to become fairly dry, when re-potting so far as may be necessary is carried out.

Prune during December or early in January for blooming about three months later.

It is important that the plants should be fairly dry and should have cool treatment before and for some time after pruning, so that conditions are made to approximate closely to those prevailing out of doors in, say, March with regard to the outdoor plants. It is only necessary just to exclude frost. A hurried start will mean weak shoots and poor blooms. If the plants have been potted up from the open ground, they must be pruned hard back the first year. All sappy, weak and crowded shoots must be removed and the well-ripened ones which remain shortened back to two or three eyes. After the first year, if the plants have made a sufficient number of well-ripened growths from the base, old wood may be removed and these growths shortened to three or four eyes. In the absence of these new growths from the base, the laterals or main shoots should be shortened back nearly to the point of the previous year's pruning cut.

The pruning of plants under glass should be much harder than is necessary for outdoor plants. Avoid leaving long shoots or a straggling unmanageable plant will be the result, whereas the aim should be to secure a well-balanced and dwarf plant with good shoots as equally distributed round it as possible.

47

PART II

ENEMIES OF THE ROSE

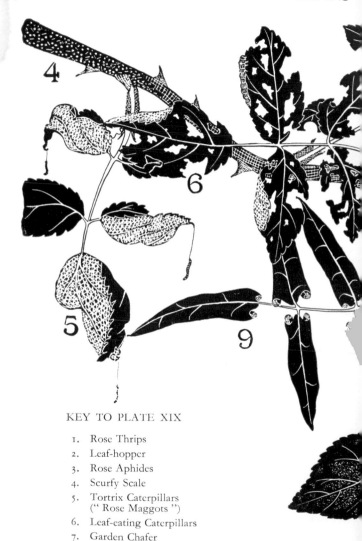

KEY TO PLATE XIX

1. Rose Thrips
2. Leaf-hopper
3. Rose Aphides
4. Scurfy Scale
5. Tortrix Caterpillars
   ("Rose Maggots")
6. Leaf-eating Caterpillars
7. Garden Chafer
8. Leaf Miner
9. Leaf-rolling Sawfly
10. Rose Slugworm Sawfly
11. Leaf-cutter Bee

ROSE

Photograph illustrating PURPLE SPOTTING due to various causes and often mistaken for Black Spot

Showing various forms of **Purple Spotting,** *none of which is true Black Spot. These purple discolorations are usually symptoms of physiological disorders, and though the exact causes are still obscure, evidence suggests that the major factors are unsuitable soil conditions and nutritional deficiencies. Susceptability to Purple Spotting varies very much with variety*

Plate XX

Rose Black Spot

Plate XX

A " close-up " of two leaflets, showing the typical " fringed " appearance of the younger spo
which is such a valuable diagnostic character

Rose Powdery Mildew Spotting

Plate XXI

Showing various stages of the Rose Powdery Mildew caused by the fungus Sphaerotheca pannos
(Waller) Lév. The leaves on the left show the small raised purple spots, a common effect of th
mildew

**Photograph illustrating true Black Spot of Rose caused by the fungus
Actinonema Rosae (Lib.) Fr.**

*showing typical forms of the Spot in various stages. The " fringed " edge of the spot is clearly
seen, particularly on the leaf in the left-hand bottom corner*

Plate XXIII

Dying back of snags left by bad pruning and at the base a stem canker which might show the black spore bodies of Coniothyrium fuckelii

Plate XXIV

PART II

ENEMIES OF THE ROSE

BY

JOHN RAMSBOTTOM

WHEN every care has been taken to ensure that rose plants have been supplied with all that is needed for their proper growth there is still the possibility of trouble from disease and from pests. There are a considerable number of these but only a few are really troublesome; the rest are usually rare, restricted in their range, and for the most part not very harmful.

DISEASES

THE three most prevalent diseases of roses are Mildew, Black Spot and Rust. They are caused by microscopic fungi—*Sphærotheca*, *Actinonema* and *Phragmidium* respectively. A few words on the nature of fungi may help in the understanding of, and consequently intelligent dealing with, the problems they give rise to. The aim of a grower is to protect his roses, either by preventing attacks, or by getting rid of them.

Fungi reproduce from spores, which have the same function as seeds. They differ from them in being microscopic, consisting essentially of a single cell and, consequently, contain no embryo. Under suitable conditions they grow, producing exceedingly fine threads (*hyphæ*, *mycelium*) which, as it were, explore the possibilities of the substratum on which they find themselves.

But why are fungi so often the cause of disease in plants (and other organisms) and destructive to food and stored products? It is simply because they have no chlorophyll, the green colouring matter which enables plants to manufacture the carbohydrates necessary for their growth—and, eventually, ours. Fungi (like man) must, therefore, obtain their carbohydrates already elaborated. There are only two sources of supply, the quick and the dead. Fungi outnumber flowering plants in every way, and this vast assemblage has certainly made the most of its opportunities. A rough division is made

49

between those which grow on living organisms (parasites) and those growing on dead or decaying matter (saprophytes).

It is a remarkable fact that a large proportion of them, both parasites and saprophytes, are specialised in their habitats. Thus a parasite fungus is usually restricted in its range of host plant, and, moreover, is most often confined to one species. This is well seen in the three diseases of the rose under consideration.

Mildews occur on various garden plants and weeds, and in some seasons are very common. There is no cause, however, to fear that mildew will spread from any of these plants to roses, for the rose Mildew (*Sphærotheca pannosa* var. *Rosæ*) is a specialised parasite of the rose, i.e. it occurs only on roses and does not spread from, or to, other plants.

The second species (*Actinonema Rosæ*), which causes Black Spot, is similarly confined to roses, both wild and cultivated. There is no similar fungus occurring on other garden plants. It is known that this species comprises a number of strains, or races, differing among other things, in their parasitic effects— but whatever strain or strains there may be they are restricted to the rose.

Rust fungi show specialisation to a remarkable degree. The one on garden roses (*Phragmidium mucronatum*) is restricted to roses. Indeed it is probable that it consists of a number of specialised races so that it is unlikely to spread from diseased wild roses in the vicinity. However this may be, the genus *Phragmidium* occurs only on members of the rose family.

Another point which needs stressing is that most fungi produce prodigious numbers of spores—literally millions. Their small size and extreme lightness ensures their ready dispersal by air currents, and gardens have a floating population of them. Insects of various kinds carry spores on their bodies as they pass from plant to plant, an unintentional spreading of a kind in which human hands and clothing may assist.

Assuming that a spore has found its billet, what happens? As already said it germinates by sending out extremely fine threads. The food in the spore is soon exhausted and the next stage is to assure further supplies. This it does by robbing the rose of the food and material that it has manufactured for its own use.

The fungus causing the diseases can be recognised by its

method of growth, the way in which its spores are formed and their size, shape and colour. But as the attacking fungi differ so do the reactions of the rose so that different diseases can be recognised on sight.

Mildew. This is the most obvious rose disease and the most common. In no season is it absent, in some it occurs in epidemic form. The whole of the leaves and stems may become covered with mildew so that they look almost as if they had been lightly dusted with flour.

The first signs of attack are whitish or greyish spots on the young leaves and stems, which often take on a reddish or purplish tinge. Spread is rapid. All the young parts affected are dwarfed and misshapen and many of the injured leaves fall. Young buds which are attacked sometimes remain unopened and growth and flower production are seriously disturbed.

The individual mycelial threads are too fine to be seen with the naked eye, but in covering a leaf in all directions they must reach an enormous length. The mycelium is superficial and the problem of procuring food from the leaf is solved by the formation of small suckers (*haustoria*) which, beginning as small pegs, penetrate the leaf cuticle and swell out within the epidermal cells, acting not only for absorption but as hold-fasts. The darkish spots usually seen after an attack are due to the death of the epidermal cells.

Over its surface the mycelium forms upright columns of barrel-shaped spores (*conidia*). These readily become detached; some are blown about, others fall into little clusters. The powdery appearance seen under a lens, or in oblique light, is due to these spores. A spore alighting on a rose leaf immediately germinates, sending out a thread-like hypha, which soon forms haustoria and, in a few days, a fresh crop of conidia.

Various roses differ much in their susceptibility to Mildew, ranging from comparative immunity in some of the glossy-leaved Wichuraiana hybrids to great susceptibility in soft-leaved quickly maturing varieties such as " Crimson Glory."

Treatment. The object of treatment is to prevent attack by a parasite, or, if this has already begun, to destroy it or restrict its action. Fungicides, i.e. substances which kill fungi, are applied as sprays or dusts. The search for satisfactory fungicides is hampered by the fact that of two organisms essentially similar, both being plants, one is to be killed while the other, with which it is intimately associated, remains unharmed. In recent years a vast amount of research has been carried out to formulate substances which will kill a specific fungus without damaging or disfiguring the host plant, be cheap and easy to apply, inoffensive, and harmless to clothing and its wearer. Whenever a trial is given to any of the new organic compounds the instructions supplied with them should be adhered to strictly.

Mildew is one of the easiest diseases to treat, for the whole of the fungus is on the surface of the rose, with the exception of the haustoria, and not buried within the tissues. Consequently a fungicide acts directly upon it. Spraying with a colloidal copper white oil emulsion is effective as a preventive or as a cure. Good results have also been obtained with an organic compound marketed as Karathane.

Black Spot. This, though not so widespread as Mildew, is very common, especially in cool, damp years. It is very destructive, so much so that often any spot or blemish on rose foliage is feared as a possible prelude to an attack. It is wise to refrain from over-anxiety about the health of one's roses; one soon becomes able to distinguish between spots that need attention and those which are of no consequence.

Black Spot most usually attacks leaves when they are more or less fully grown, and appears as black or purplish spots on their upper surface. It shows first as minute black specks which gradually enlarge and, normally, become roundish, about a quarter of an inch across, with a very irregular fringed border and radiating fibrils over the surface; sometimes, however, they may extend over the whole of a leaflet. As the disease progresses numerous minute, shining black dots, arranged in concentric circles appear on the surface of the spot. These are the fructifications of the fungus where the spores are formed; each of them contains several thousands of spores.

Blown on to a rose leaf the spore gives rise to colourless threads which penetrate the cuticle and enter the epidermal cells. Here they remain localised for the most part, though they advance somewhat both laterally and vertically. As they age their colour changes through yellow to brown but never becomes black. The dark appearance of Black Spot is not due to the colour of the fungus but to the presence of a brown substance in the outer portions of the epidermis, which is a product of the degeneration of the cell contents. (Similarly, with some of the less important leaf diseases of roses; the different appearances of the spots, which at once give a clue to their cause, result from the reaction of the rose to the destructive action of the parasite—the symptoms of the disease.)

The infecting thread expands laterally just within the outermost layer of the epidermal cell wall and forms strands which give the appearance of radiating fibrils on the surface of the spot. About a fortnight after infection, spores are formed at the ends of short hyaline columns which arise vertically from the surface of the pads. The upward growth of the columns first raises the cuticle into a dome shape and then ruptures it. and so liberates the spores. These are blown about by air currents or transported on insects, and so infection spreads.

The main damage seems to result not from the compact fungal mass under the epidermis but from hyphæ which extend from this into the inner tissues of the leaf. These hyphæ presumably absorb food from the contents of the cells into which they enter and transfer it to the main mass of the fungus.

Separate spots on leaves are doubtless the result of different spore infections; where leaves are completely covered there have presumably not only been multiple infections but a joining up of adjacent patches. When there is heavy infection the leaves are shed much earlier than normally. In some varieties, however, the leaves fall very shortly after infection, even as soon as early June.

If defoliation occurs a crop of fresh leaves is usually formed from the buds at the ends of the branches which should remain dormant until the next season. Not only is the plant weakened by this, but the new leaves are very commonly attacked by Mildew at a very early stage.

Despite common belief the fungus can extend, in certain varieties at least, to all aerial organs—stipules, petioles, sepals and petals. The fact that stems can be affected is of importance in connection with the control of the disease. Infected stems have a blackened blistered appearance, the pustules being dotted with fructifications. The vegetative mycelium develops entirely in the cortex, which it kills, sometimes producing deep-seated cavities that become filled with spores.

Treatment. The first care should be given to what might be called sanitation. Leaves which have fallen after being attacked by the fungus bear a multitude of spores on their surface, and these may indeed continue to be produced for some time. Obviously these spores act as sources of further infection; it requires only a single spore deposited on a healthy moist leaf to cause Black Spot—and there may be millions. Therefore all such infected leaves should be collected carefully and burned; also any fallen infected parts. Diseased stems and twigs may be pruned, but if this is done it must be circumspect for it is never to be overlooked that a rose gains much of its essential food from its leaves and a plant weakened by disease cannot afford to lose any that are active.

Black Spot is not so easy to control as is Mildew, for the fungus causing it lives within the tissue, breaking forth to the surface only when spore production begins.

Many different fungicides have been used to combat the disease in the past but with no very marked success. Of these, probably spraying with a colloidal copper white oil emulsion has given the best results. The most promising fungicide is one of the new complex organic compounds which has the trade name captan (amongst others) and is marketed here as Orthocide. A trace kills the spores or renders then inactive. It is remarkably safe both on plants and on the operator. Its only drawback is that it is somewhat pungent and causes irritation when inhaled. It is compatible with most insecticides except those containing oils or highly alkaline substances. Thus it should not be used on plants which have been treated with colloidal copper oil emulsion to control Mildew or Rust. As with all proprietary preparations Orthocide should be used with strict adherence to the instructions supplied.

Attacks of Black Spot, like those of Mildew, vary according to the variety of rose. *Rosa wichuraiana* is thought to be immune, and many varieties having this species in their ancestry have inherited this character.

A search is being made for other immune species of *Rosa* with a view to breeding garden varieties which would remain

54

free from infection under all conditions. About half a dozen have been found which are said to be immune, and about the same number reported as highly resistant.

Research work on these lines is not only full of pitfalls but is a long-term job. No rose has yet been bred in which the highly desirable quality of immunity has been incorporated together with the outstanding characters of modern varieties. It is mentioned here mainly to stress the seriousness with which Black Spot is considered by growers of roses.

Rust. The third disease to be considered is puzzling in its incidence. It almost seems as if it occurs in some kind of cycle for it may be very rare in several seasons and then burst out and cause great damage for two or three years, particularly in districts where there are early and heavy formations of dew. No variety of cultivated rose appears to be immune, and hardy hybrid varieties seem particularly susceptible. Badly infected plants often die in the first year of infection.

For present purposes the story can be shortened into a consideration of the three stages of the life-cycle which can be recognised with the naked eye: (*a*) æcidiospores, (*b*) uredospores, (*c*) teleutospores; three kinds of spore, differing in their origin, and in their function.

(*a*) The first stage is seen in early spring as small rust-coloured pustule-like swellings on the under surface of the leaf, which often become confluent. Within these are closely packed columns of rust-coloured spores (*æcidiospores*) which are set free when the epidermis of the leaf is ruptured. These spores are able to grow immediately and bring about infection.

Pustules may also be produced on petioles, sepals and even on the hips. What is more important, however, is that they are often formed on stems, arising from fungal threads which may remain alive for some years producing a steady and annual crop of æcidiospores. Usually the patches of Rust are larger here than on the leaves, frequently up to an inch or more in length, irregular in shape, causing distortion and curving and often destroying the buds; in winter the spore-producing layer is covered with bark. When the fungus disappears from the cracks gaping wounds are left which are potential centres of infection by other injurious fungi, particularly those of canker.

(*b*) About June another spore form appears (*uredospore*). This, like the æcidiospore, is bright orange-coloured, but the spores are borne singly, not in chains. They germinate immediately they are shed and rapidly propagate the parasite, and are probably the main source of new infections.

(*c*) The third spore stage, the *teleutospore*, follows on about August from the same pad of fungal threads which previously bore the uredospores. Formerly a bright orange, the spot gradually darkens until it is almost black. This is due to the colour of the teleutospores. These are much larger than the uredospores, elongated and not globose, with a thickened not a thin cell wall, and divided by cross septa into six to nine cells. As the uredospore is a summer spore adapted in every way for aiding in the rapid spread of the fungus, so the teleutospore is a winter spore or resting spore able to withstand the rigours of temperature and drought and carry the fungus over to another growing season: indeed it seems to require freezing before it will germinate.

Germination takes place in the spring. A tube is put forth from each portion of the spore, but does not continue in growth to form a thread which could bring about infection. Instead the tubes become septate and each of the cells so formed produces a small hyaline spore (*sporidium*): this, alighting on a rose plant, germinates and sends out a thread which penetrates the leaf and eventually gives rise to a pustule containing æcidiospores.

Thus we have: sporidium (spore formed by teleutospore)→ æcidiospore → uredospore → teleutospore → sporidium.

Treatment. It is clear that as fallen infected leaves still harbour the fungus they are a continued source of infection: if teleutospores are present the fungus will be tided over until young leaves are developing in the spring. All leaves should be collected from the ground and burned—the removal of badly diseased leaves still on the plant is advisable. The soil under the infected rose should be turned over so that any teleutospores lying on the soil will be covered up and so rendered harmless.

The other, and possibly the main source of overwintering, is the lesions on the stems. Whenever possible these should be treated surgically, always remembering that the threads of the fungus are present in the tissues below the wound.

Mildew

Sphaerotheca pannosa Lév.

Plate XXV

Black Spot

Actinonema rosae Fr.

Plate XXVI

Rust

Phragmidium mucronatum (Pers.) Schlecht
Showing underside of leaf

Plate XXVII

Chlorosis

Plate XXVIII

No entirely satisfactory treatment is yet proved for Rust on roses though preliminary trials with thiram and ganeb have given good results. Colloidal cuprous oxide oil emulsion is sometimes satisfactory. In spraying it is essential that the underside of the leaf should be properly covered for it is there that the fungus shows.

Chlorosis. This is the term used to describe the condition in which leaves and stems lose their green colouring matter and become yellow, either wholly or in part. As it is the chlorophyll which enables a plant to manufacture the carbohydrates necessary for growth, its lack causes malnutrition, defoliation, and eventually death.

Yellowing in roses can result from overwatering and poor drainage, insect attack, or insufficient light. The most usual cause, however, is the deficiency in certain soils of one or more chemical elements which, because of the small amount needed, are known as trace elements, minor elements or micronutrients. Thus, for the most part, chlorosis is a physiological disease, differing from those already considered in that it is not caused by a pathogenic organism but results from an upsetting of the normal processes in some way or other.

It has long been known that a trace of iron is necessary for chlorophyll formation, but it is only in recent years, indeed since the shortage of stable manure, that the importance of other trace elements has been realised. " Artificial " fertilisers aim chiefly at supplying nitrogen, phosphorus, and potassium, the so-called " fertiliser " elements; calcium, magnesium and sulphur are needed in less quantities.

There has been a good deal of research into the part played by trace elements generally, of which nine or ten have been recognised and the definite symptoms in growing plants charted so that, as these are often very characteristic, a preliminary diagnosis is possible.

The chief deficiencies met with in rose-growing are nitrogen, potassium and iron; manganese deficiency occurs on certain soils; magnesium deficiency has also been observed.

Chlorosis due to iron deficiency was the first to be recognised. The symptoms are the gradual loss of green colour in the leaves, which become a sickly yellow. Usually it appears towards the end of spring, beginning frequently between the veins and along the borders of the younger leaves; the stem also shows yellow patches, which become confluent. The whole of the leaf usually yellows, but occasionally some parts remain green and a speckled appearance results. The leaves shrivel and fall and the plant produces weedy shoots and a crop of stunted leaves before it finally starves to death.

Most soils contain sufficient iron for the plant's needs but a number of factors may make it unavailable. As a rule the application of lime to a soil increases the availability of fertiliser elements, especially in highly organic soils. Excess of lime leads to decreased availability of trace elements, nearly all of which become less available with alkalinity.

In a soil which is highly alkaline, an over-abundance of calcium or phosphate will tie up the iron in the form of insoluble iron hydroxides, carbonates and phosphates—insoluble, therefore unavailable to the plant. This is the reason for iron chlorosis where there is a chalky subsoil, or gross overliming. Many methods have been tried to counteract this induced iron deficiency with no real satisfaction. The most recent, and the most promising, is by adding iron chelates to the soil. Chelating agents are organic compounds which surround metal ions and hold them in water-soluble form. Iron has been combined with several amino-acid types of chelating agents to form iron chelates which are stable in the soil, and have proved very effective in correcting iron chlorosis in plants growing on acid and neutral soils: the iron is in a form available to the roots. Iron chelates are marketed as Sequestrene Iron. They are soluble in water and are best applied to the soil, though at low strengths they can be used as foliar sprays.

Other chelated metallic trace elements are available. As manganese deficiency often runs parallel to that of iron, a mixture of the sequestrenes of iron and manganese together with active magnesium is sold as Sequestrene Plus. This should prove of particular value on chalky soils.

As always, instructions supplied with the proprietary preparations should be followed with particular care.

CANKER AND DIE-BACK

BY

APHRA P. WILSON

Canker and Die-back are terms used to describe certain visual symptoms relating to localised unhealthy and breakdown conditions on the wood; they do not designate specific fungus diseases. Many cankers have fungi associated with them, but these fungi are generally invaders which can increase the size of an affected area but are not its initial cause. Most " canker " fungi are in fact " wound " fungi.

Canker indicates a localised breakdown on the wood which starts in tissue under the bark on a main stem or on a branch. Eventually the death and collapse of this tissue forms a sunken area (canker), which is usually tinted with or delineated by brown, red or purple colorations. Sometimes the bark in the centre of the canker becomes loose, cracks and peels off and the canker becomes bounded by a ridge of corky, wound callus, produced by the surrounding healthy tissue. The cankered area may extend in size and can completely girdle the stem or branch, in which case the portion beyond the canker dies, owing to interference with its supplies of food and water. If a cankered area develops below a bud, the bud will die for the same reason.

Die-back describes a condition in which the tip of a branch becomes unhealthy and dies, a process which continues back down the branch to a lower node, to a larger branch or in extreme conditions right back to ground level. The term Die-back is often used, albeit erroneously, to denote the dying back of cut branches or of snags.

The Causes of Canker and Die-back

Canker. The basic causes of wood breakdown are (1) penetration of the protective bark, and (2) unbalanced nutrition. Bark penetration can be caused by mechanical damage, unhealed cuts, thorn and other wounds, and by attacks by insects or by Black Spot and Rust fungi on the wood. Unbalanced nutrition can cause breakdown of the wood tissue under the bark with subsequent bark cracking, failure of cut surfaces to callus properly and premature leaf fall which results in weak or dead buds. All these conditions can allow entrance to "wound" fungi, which must first become established on dead tissue before they can attack the living wood.

Die-back. On roses, except sometimes on ramblers, Die-back is due to such factors as frost, bad drainage, canker formation lower down the branch, the aftermath of Rose Mildew attack on the shoot and to unbalanced nutrition.

Rose Cankers and the Fungi Associated With Them

Stem Canker (*Leptosphæria coniothyrium* (Fuckel) Sacc.)

Common and destructive. It starts as a red-tinged, yellow, pimply, water-soaked area with a reddish margin. Later, the area turns brown, becomes sunken, the bark cracks exposing the wood and a ridge of corky wound callus replaces the red margin. The summer spore stage of the fungus (*Coniothyrium fuckelii* Sacc.) produces black pycnidia containing dark brown spores which give the canker a sooty look.

Bud Canker (*Griphosphæria corticola* (Fuckel) Höhnel)

Starts as a small brown sunken area, with a purple margin, round a dead bud or a thorn scar. Later the bark in the centre of the canker dies and shrinks but the wood is not exposed. The canker extends in size and can girdle the branch, but it remains smooth with little or no callus. The fungus perithecia have thin black necks which are visible through the shrivelled bark.

Crown Canker (*Cylindrocladium scoparium.* Morgan)

More common in the U.S.A. than in the U.K. The first sign is a discoloured water-soaked area at or just above the union of the scion and the stock, which becomes black and can spread to the stem or to the roots. Later cracks appear in the canker, extend to the wood, become deeper and swelling occurs in the area. Old cankers have a conspicuous powdery appearance. The fungus has only summer spores which are large, cylindrical and held together by a sticky slime.

Brand Canker (*Coniothyrium wernsdorffiæ.* Laubert)

Recorded from Germany, Italy and the U.S.A. and occasionally from Scotland. Occurs chiefly where rose bushes are protected at their bases during winter by heaps of soil or leaves. First sign is a light brown area surrounded by a purple margin on the base of a one-year or older shoot in winter or in early spring. Later, the areas take on the characteristic black burnt look. The summer spore stage of the fungus (pycnidia) are visible as minute pimples on the canker.

Brown Canker (*Cryptosporella umbrina* (Jenk.) Jenkins and Wehm)

Recorded from the U.S.A., rare in the U.K. First seen on young stems as circular reddish spots which turn white and form patches. These later become chestnut-brown cankers surrounded by deep purple margins. In damp conditions the pycnidia of the fungus exude light yellow-brown coils of summer spores.

Die-back of Rambler Roses (*Gnomonia rubi* (Rehm.) Wint)

Recorded, but not common in the U.K. The long shoots show black patches and die from the tip downwards, the leaves turn yellow and fall early. Ash-grey areas with vivid purple borders develop between the black patches and the green stem. Can kill shoots to ground level. The hair-like necks of the fungus perithecia protrude through the bark and are visible.

Prevention and Control

The causes of Canker and Die-back, indicated above, give the key to preventive and control measures. The particular fungus present is of little practical interest to the rose grower as the treatment is the same for all.

All cuts should be cleanly made and to an eye (see Plate XII(D)) and all dead and dying wood removed and burnt. Damage to rose bushes by cultivators, hoes, etc., should be avoided and proper spray precautions taken against Black Spot and Rust and against insect pests, especially green-fly.

Deep or frequent digging of rose beds can damage the feeding roots, as can bad drainage or waterlogging.

Where cankers are persistent, the bushes may need supplies of calcium, phosphate and magnesium in addition to that already given in the usual fertilisers. Ground chalk or gypsum will supply calcium and there is some in nitro-chalk. Phosphate and calcium are supplied by basic slag or superphosphate, and magnesium by epsom salts applied as a soil dressing or as a spray.

Garden hygiene, good pruning and balanced nutrition are all most essential to keeping rose bushes healthy and avoiding Canker and Die-back.

Graft Disease or Canker (*Coniothyrium rosarium*. Cooke and Harkness)

More of a disease than a canker. The control consists in using healthy scions and stocks, keeping the union above the soil level and using a good grafting (or budding) method. Occurs chiefly in the U.S.A.; also in the U.K.

The first sign is a light yellowish water-soaked area on the scion or just above the union. The area spreads, turns dark brown and later light brown in colour. The fungus pycnidia are produced in the light area. If the lesion girdles the scion it wilts suddenly and dies; if not, the graft grows one-sided and makes a poor bush. The fungus is very similar to, and may even be identical with, *Coniothyrium fuckelii* Sacc., the summer stage of the fungus associated with stem canker.

PESTS

MANY different kinds of insect are to be found on roses, as on most plants. Some cause much damage, others are of small significance. There is little specialisation, or to put it otherwise, few insects occur only on the rose.

Damage from pests is usually immediately apparent whereas disease may have got well under way before it becomes obvious. This is due to the difference in structure and mode of life between parasitic fungus and insect pest. The first is absolutely dependent on the rose throughout its life, and usually has its working parts within the tissues, nothing being seen externally until its life-history is completed by the production of spores: it has no separate existence. Insects, on the other hand, are independent and free. They may lay their eggs on the rose and these develop there, but they feed by detaching portions or by sucking juices, a way of obtaining food which is more easily understood than that of fungal threads which have to absorb all their food as liquid through their cell walls. Thus Green Fly punctures leaves and sucks up juices whereas the fungus of Black Spot penetrates the epidermis and cell walls by means of enzymes, which similarly act on the cell contents so that these are in a suitable state to be absorbed by osmosis: there is never an open passage, there is never any pumping action. Pests themselves are always spoken of, as Green Fly, Sawfly, Thrips—not what they do. On the other hand, it is the disease of the rose—Mildew, Black Spot, Rust—that we refer to, not the fungus that brings this about. A parasitic fungus *infects* and causes disease; an insect *infests* and causes damage.

If we were considering all the insects known to have caused damage to roses the list would be so long that it would be necessary to enter into their scientific classifications. Only the commoner ones, however, need mention here—those that are shown in the accompanying plate.

One or two points about insects in general will help towards the understanding of the particular life histories, and also the different methods of control to be adopted.

Insects have no lungs and breathe by means of an elaborate system of air tubes which branch throughout the organism and are joined to breathing pores (*spiracles*) arranged along the sides of the body.

Most insects cause damage by biting and chewing, which they are able to do because of the structure of their mouths. The rest have mouth parts modified to enable the piercing of tissues and the extraction of cell contents.

Most insects emerge from the egg in a very different form from the adult. The growth changes that take place are termed metamorphosis. The higher forms, such as moths, wasps and bees pass through what is called complete metamorphosis; the egg hatches into an active feeding, growing larva (a caterpillar, grub or maggot) so different from the adult that it seems incredible that the one can grow into the other. After this period of growth and feeding it becomes immobile—the pupa or chrysalis; during this stage of outward inactivity there is a complete change, both externally and internally, resulting in the active, sexually mature and, generally, winged adult insect.

In other forms such as Aphids, Thrips and Capsid Bugs, there is incomplete metamorphosis. Here the egg hatches into a nymph, which usually resembles its parents except that it is smaller, wingless, and sexually immature. The nymph undergoes a series of moults and wings develop. When fully fed it passes into a partial pupal stage and then into the fully formed adult insect. Thus here there is gradual transformation from the young to the adult, and feeding goes on without a break.

Aphids, Green Fly (Fig. 3). Several species of Aphid attack roses, some so common and widely distributed that no garden seems to be without them. They occur chiefly on the underside of leaves, on young shoots and flower buds—though one species infests the roots. Some remain on the rose throughout the year, while others, after a period, migrate to a variety of different plants.

The commonest species on cultivated roses is the Rose aphid (*Macrosiphon rosæ*). Eggs are laid on the plants by oviparous females in late autumn. In spring these give rise to " stem mothers " which are all female and produce living young (parthenogenetically) which soon mature, and themselves give rise to females. Sooner or later a winged generation of females is formed which fly off to teasels as well as to other roses; here they rapidly produce such large colonies of wingless females as to completely cover the shoots. In late summer and early autumn winged " return migrants " arise which produce a brood of wingless egg-laying females which are fertilised by winged males appearing at about the same time. Eggs are formed and deposited, at first pale-straw colour but soon becoming shining black. The wingless female is green or red with long black cornicles (honey-tubes) and a yellowish green tail.

Penetration of the leaf is made by two pairs of needle-like stylets which, when not in use, are neatly tucked away in a groove in the lower lip; the stylets reach the vascular bundles and tap the phloem for the food it contains. Feeding is continuous, for large amounts of cell sap have to be imbibed to secure sufficient nutriment. In this process far more sugar and other substances are acquired than can be used. These pass directly through the digestive system and are deposited as what is known as honey-dew. This sweet sticky liquid—a puzzle to the ancients—not only makes foliage unpleasant in appearance and to the touch but serves as an attraction for ants, bees, flies, and also moulds.

Aphids have many natural enemies. Tits and sparrows search diligently for them. Everyone must have noticed how two-spotted and seven-spotted ladybirds feed on them during summer, and their larvæ (" niggers ") do the same. Several species of hover-fly lay their eggs in the colonies, and larvæ feed on them; thus also the attractive lace-wing flies with their strange stalked eggs growing on the leaves. Ichneumon flies deposit their eggs within the aphid and their larvæ feed as internal parasites; the adult insect, emerging through a small circular hole, leaves the dried empty yellowish skin adhering to shoot or leaf. Despite these checks aphids flourish and it is essential to take direct measures against them early in the season before large populations are built up and before their natural enemies appear.

Thrips (Fig. 1), known also as Thunder-flies and Black-flies, are serious pests, especially in hot dry summers, swarming over all parts above ground and causing a mottled and marbled effect on the leaves, distortion of young shoots and discoloration of buds and flowers, particularly along the margin of the petals. The adult insect is small, seldom more than one-tenth of an inch long, black or dark brown. It has two pairs of narrow wings fringed profusely with fine, long hairs and bead-like antennæ. The mouth parts are modified but not so completely as the stylets of aphids; they are adapted for rasping the surface layers of leaves and shoots, breaking up the tissues and sucking up the mashed food. The eggs, which are larger than one would expect, are inserted within the tissues of leaves, shoots and flowers. The nymphs resemble the parents but are wingless, and vary from pale to reddish yellow.

Rose Thrips (*Thrips fuscipennis*) overwinters under glass in crevices of brickwork, woodwork, and beneath the bark of old stems. A few adults may continue to feed throughout the winter in heated houses. Injury to forced blooms may be severe in the early part of the season, the eggs being deposited within the tissues of the outer petals as the calyx begins to open out, causing malformation, as well as in young foliage. Outdoor plants may suffer similar injury during the summer.

Flower Thrips (*Frankliniella intonsa*) attacks flower buds and open blooms during hot dry spells in summer and early autumn.

Rose Leaf-Hopper (Fig. 2). The occurrence of pale, mottled areas on rose leaves during spring and summer, together with cast or moult skins (" ghost fly ") on the underside indicate the presence of the Rose Leaf-hopper (*Typhlocyba rosæ*). A severe attack causes premature leaf-fall, especially in climbing roses, and results in a severe check to growth.

The pale yellowish insect is very active, jumping and taking flying leaps into the air when disturbed. The eggs are inserted beneath the epidermis of the leaf, up to four being laid near together in May and June. All stages occur on the under-side of leaves during summer. The almost colourless, wingless nymphs suck the sap and cause a series of mottled or marbled areas on the upper leaf surface. A second brood appears in late August and September but does less injury than the first generation.

Hoppers overwinter mainly in the nymphal and pupal stages, but adults may survive in crevices of trellis and brickwork.

Scale Insects (Fig. 4). Shoots and stems of wild and cultivated roses are frequently encrusted with scale insects, including the Scurfy, Brown and Nut Scales, especially in neglected bushes.

The commonest is the Scurfy Scale (*Aulacaspis rosæ*), particularly on briars used as stocks, where it appears as flat

66

whitish scales, the females round, the males elongated and smaller. The minute adult two-winged males appear during early summer and pair with the wingless females, the eggs being laid beneath the scaly covering during July and early August. The orange-coloured nymphs crawl from beneath the old female scale and wander about freely for a time, giving the stems the appearance of having been dusted with red pepper. They then settle down and insert their long piercing stylets into the tissues and feed on the juices they extract. Their bodies become covered with a scaly structure which becomes round or elongate according to whether it is female or male.

Not only is a severe infestation unsightly but it severely checks growth.

Moths (Figs. 5, 6 and 8). The adults live on a liquid diet, nectar, fruit juices, honey, and so on, inbibed through their tubular sucking proboscis, while the larva (caterpillar) has biting mouth parts which enables it to chew. It is, therefore, the caterpillar which does the damage to plants. Many have been recorded on roses, but only a few are major pests.

Injury to roses is of different types: (i) partial or complete defoliation (Buff-tip, Lackey, Vapourer and Winter Moths); (ii) Tortrix Moths or " Rose Maggots "; (iii) bud and flower injury (Tortrix Moths); (iv) leaf-skeletonising (Yellow-tail and Buff-tip Moths); and (v) leaf-mining (Rose Leaf-miner Moth).

Chafer Beetles (Fig. 7). Four species of chafers are associated with roses: the Cockchafer or " May Bug," Rose Chafer, Garden Chafer or " Bracken Clock," and, to a lesser extent, the Summer Chafer.

The adult chafers often appear in vast swarms during May and June and attack the foliage, flower buds and open blooms of roses. The larvæ live in the soil and feed on the roots and underground stems of a great variety of plants.

The Cockchafer is a large beetle with black head and thorax, reddish brown slightly hairy wing cases with five raised parallel lines on each, and clubbed tips to the antennæ. The larva (" White Grubb " or " Joe Bassett ") is thick, fleshy, dirty white with the last segments of the abdomen swollen and dark purplish brown. The light lemon head bears a strong pair of mandibles or jaws used for severing roots and girdling underground stems, thus cutting off food supplies to the rest of the plant. It lies in the soil in a curved position but can move with ease, especially in light sandy ground. The fully-fed larva is about one and a half inches long. The Chafers fly at dusk. The eggs are laid in the ground, preferably in sandy soil. The grubs continue to feed until the third or fourth year; during cold weather they cease feeding and descend to a considerable depth in light soils. They eventually pupate in earthen cells, and the resultant Chafers emerge during May and June and feed on the foliage of trees. The Rose Chafer is smaller, with striking, metallic bright golden green wing cases and thorax, the wing cases flecked with white. The larva resembles that of a Cockchafer but its body is clothed with rows of reddish hair; it is fully fed within two to three years. The adult feeds on rose blooms, devouring the petals and anthers and, to some extent, the leaves. The grubs eat the young roots and partially sever the larger roots.

The Garden Chafer is the smallest of the four, one-third to one-half inch in length. The thorax is a metallic bluish green and the wing cases reddish brown. The larva is proportionately smaller and lives only one year. The adults fly in bright sunshine in June, often in large swarms. They feed on the flower buds and open blooms of roses, and on other plants; the larva attacks roots particularly of grasses.

The Summer Chafer is a little larger, three-eighths of an inch long, reddish brown and with a hairy body. The larva lives for two, sometimes three years, feeding like the Garden Chafer, on roots. The adults feed on rose blooms and may cause considerable damage.

Sawflies. About seventy species occur on roses, some confined to stems, others infesting Rosaceous plants generally. Several are common and important. The Leaf-Rolling Rose Sawfly (*Blennocampa pusilla*) (Fig. 9) is one of the most destructive pests causing complete lateral folding of the leaflets, and a consequent interference with their manufacture of food, and premature leaf-fall.

The black shining adults, resembling somewhat Queen Ants, appear in May and early June. After pairing, the female straddles the unfolding leaflet and inserts an egg in the tissue near the margin. In doing this a toxin is injected to which the leaflet reacts, some days before the eggs hatch, by an inward and downward rolling.

The young larva is very pale green or whitish, becoming greener, with pale areas between the segments, conspicuous short hairs along the back of the body, and a white or brown, very shiny head, with a conspicuous eye-spot. It feeds on the parts of the rolled foliage, usually only one larva to each leaflet, but it may move to another when the food supply is exhausted.

The Rose Slug Sawfly (*Endelomyia æthiops*) (Fig. 10) causes much injury to roses. The adult fly is shining black and appears from mid-May to mid-June, and also in July and August. The eggs are laid in the serrations of the young leaf edge, usually one a leaf. There are two broods of larvæ, June and July, and August and September. The larva is yellowish but the green contents of the food canal can be seen through the skin. It feeds from the upper surface of the leaf and devours the whole of the internal tissue, leaving only the thin upper epidermis; the " skeletonised " leaf dries up and turns brown. The fully fed larva descends to the ground and constructs a cocoon in which it pupates the following spring.

Leaf-cutting Bees (Fig. 11). There are nine species of Leaf-cutting Bee in the country, at least three of which damage roses; the commonest is *Megachile centuncularis*. They resemble hive bees but are rather more robust, with broader heads and more hairy bodies. The female, by use of her jaw, cuts out a piece of leaf of the required shape leaving a neat smooth edge: petals also may be affected. The brood cells of the nest are made entirely of leaves and are thimble-shaped with a lid. The tunnels are formed in decaying wood and the burrow may reach a foot deep with the brood cells placed end to end from the bottom upwards. An egg is laid in each cell and the larvæ feed on pollen and honey stored there.

Treatment

In dealing with insect attacks in small gardens it is well to remember that it is possible to do a lot towards getting over them by the old methods of the cottage gardener. Hand-picking of caterpillars and eggs, indeed of anything large enough to be so dealt with (even green fly) are not to be scoffed at. But thumb-and-finger methods are for removal, not squashing, for pressing young parts of the plant may cause damage.

Sprays and dusts should be poisonous to the insect, but harmless to the rose and operator, and must be properly used. Sprays should be applied as "mists"; these give good covering without drenching and reduce run-off and dripping.

As several pests can best be prevented or controlled by the same substance the various methods are here grouped together. It is difficult to draw sharply-defined limits to the action of different poisons, but it is customary and useful to distinguish between stomach poisons and contact poisons. Stomach poisons are sucked up and produce their effect by being absorbed by the digestive tract; they are protective insecticides and useful in preventing leaf-eating. Contact poisons usually enter through the body wall or the respiratory system and affect nerve and respiratory centres and blood-stream; they are useful chiefly against sucking insects.

A third type, systemic poisons, will probably be much used when they are further developed. It has been found that certain chemicals when placed on the leaves are absorbed by the plant and, further, when watered round the roots are taken up by them and passed through the plant. If the substances are poisonous to insects the plant is protected against them. A systemic insecticide either passes unaltered with the sap stream or may bring about certain changes in the constitution of the plant which renders it harmful to insects. The chief success so far has been with phosphorus compounds but they are too poisonous for ordinary purposes, though the recently introduced Tritox is said to be innocuous. Much research is afoot to find antibiotics which will act as systemic fungicides.

Since its introduction DDT has provided an efficient treatment against insect pests in general, though it is in-effective against green fly. For the small grower it should be regarded as the most useful insecticide, and always worth trying either as a dust, or as the basis of a solution for spraying.

Green fly. Lindane, malathion and diazinon are amongst the insecticides of proved efficiency against aphids; they are applied as dusts, or included in sprays. Contact washes such as nicotine, derris, pyrethrum and white (petroleum) oils are also effective.

Thrips. Leaf-hoppers. DDT is effective. Also contact washes as for green fly.

Scurfy scale. Prune and burn infested stems. In early autumn, during the immature nymphal stages of the insect, drench with white oil and nicotine emulsion, or winter wash with tar oil or lime sulphur. DDT or malathion are effective in spring, or the contact washes as for green fly.

Caterpillars. Hand-pick, or spray with DDT emulsion to which pyrethrum extract may be added. Rose maggots (Tortrix moth larvæ) if leaf rolling has begun, can be reached only by volatile poison such as nicotine dust at high air temperatures. Attacks by leaf miners apparently cannot be circumvented; it is advisable to collect and burn infected leaves as soon as an attack is noticed.

Chafer. DDT emulsion plus pyrethrum. Collect and destroy grubs.

Sawflies. DDT emulsion plus pyrethrum. Remove and burn any rolled leaves early in the season before the eggs hatch.

Leaf-cutting Bees. No effective control other than by netting the bee while at work, or by destroying the nest.

RECENT DEVELOPMENTS IN DISEASE CONTROL

BY

E. F. ALLEN

IN recent years many new fungicides have come on to the market and some of these make it easier to control rose diseases without the foliage scorch which was sometimes associated with the older materials. Most of these newer fungicides are organic chemicals of relatively complicated structure with correspondingly confusing chemical names. Fortunately, however, the British Standards Institution have approved a series of concise common names and the more helpful manufacturers quote these on their labels.

These common names refer to the active ingredient, which is responsible for the disease control, but before this can be used by the gardener it is usually necessary to mix it with a wetting agent, in the case of sprays, or a finely ground carrier diluent for dusting.

It is perhaps natural that each manufacturer should consider his own formulation, to which he gives a proprietary name, to be the best and certainly differences do exist, but it is not easy for the layman to evaluate these. In general, it may be said that relative efficiency of any particular fungicide will vary with the following factors:

1. The technical ability or " know-how " of the manufacturer.

2. The uniformity and fineness of a wettable powder or dust.

3. The absence of grit.

4. The type and amount of wetting agent used in a wettable powder. Too little reduces efficiency—especially with hard water—whereas too much may cause leaf scorch and will facilitate the washing off of the material from the leaves by rain.

5. The percentage of the active ingredient in the formulation.

6. The compatibility of the formulation with various insecticides or other materials which the gardener may wish to apply at the same time.

Factors 1 and 4 are clearly linked and the experienced gardener should assess these from his knowledge of a particular firm's products which he may have used in the past.

Factors 2 and 3 may be judged objectively by careful examination of the product.

Factor 5 has an effect on the retail price and the critical gardener will naturally choose a formulation which has the percentage of the active ingredient clearly stated on the label. Information on factor 6 should likewise appear on the label.

The Newer Fungicides

Captan. This is now well known to rosarians as an effective protectant against Black Spot which is very kind to the foliage. It is obtainable in retail packs as a 50 per cent wettable powder. Captan has no effect against Rust or Mildew.

Dinocap. This is effective against all powdery mildews and Rose Mildew on outdoor roses provided that the spray interval does not exceed ten days when the disease is active. It is perhaps better known by the proprietary name of Karathane, but is also sold commercially as Crotothane. The normal formulation is a 25 per cent wettable powder; as a dust it is much less effective.

Zineb and Maneb. These are the zinc and manganese salts respectively of ethylene bisdithiocarbamate and they are related to the older thiram. Both are highly efficient mild fungicides which give protection against Black Spot and Rust. Although they are reputed to have some effect against Rose Mildew, this is negligible in practice. Zineb is the cheaper of the two materials and is used extensively by growers overseas. It has been postulated that both materials decompose on the leaf surface to produce the same active fungicide, yet field experiments in the United States indicate that maneb may be slightly more effective than zineb against Black Spot.

The Older Materials

Copper. A colloidal copper preparation formulated with a petroleum white oil (Bouisol White Oil) is still one of the best and cheapest fungicides for use on roses in country gardens. Not only does it give protection against Black Spot and Rust, but it appears to be at least as effective as dinocap against Rose Mildew. As compared with the new organic fungicides, it has two disadvantages: first, it may cause leaf scorch in industrial areas because the white oil reacts with atmospheric sulphur oxides; secondly, dosage is more critical and leaf damage may occur unless care has been taken early in the season to build up to full strength over about three sprays.

Sulphur. This has often been said to be specific against powdery mildews and certainly when the element is vaporized in a glasshouse it will give almost complete control of Rose Mildew. However, when used as a spray outdoors even the modern mild or colloidal sulphurs are much less satisfactory as they frequently cause leaf scorch on many varieties.